Harald Seeger

Schülerbuch Stufe 1

Gilde-Buchhandlung Carl Kayser, Buchhandlung und Verlag GmbH, Bonn,
Bundesrepublik Deutschland, in Zusammenarbeit mit dem
Bundesverwaltungsamt, Zentralstelle für das Auslandsschulwesen, Köln.

ISBN 3-86035-010-2
Bestellnummer 010

Druck: PPK – Partner für Print und Kommunikation GmbH, 33689 Bielefeld
Printed in Germany

Vorwort

Als Alternative zu dem bisherigen Grundkurs der **K**(ompakt)-Fassung von VORWÄRTS INTERNATIONAL (K 1, K 2) wurde auf Veranlassung und unter Mitwirkung des Bundesverwaltungsamts - Zentralstelle für das Auslandsschulwesen in Köln ein gänzlich neu konzipierter Lehrgang in zwei Bänden entwickelt: **Wer? Wie? Was?**

Dieser neue Grundkurs

- berücksichtigt Erfahrungsberichte und Verbesserungsvorschläge von Lehrern und Arbeitsgruppen an Deutschen Schulen im Ausland, die Defizite bei der Arbeit mit dem alten Grundkurs feststellten;
- bezieht neuere Ergebnisse der Pragmalinguistik ein und trägt dem heutigen Stand der Fremdsprachendidaktik und -methodik Rechnung;
- ist nicht einer bestimmten Methode verpflichtet, sondern bietet durch verschiedenartige Arbeitsvorschläge breiten Spielraum für die Gestaltung des Unterrichts.
  So kann in der hier vorliegenden ersten Stufe des neuen Grundkurses bei der Einführung der Vorstellungstexte nach der audiovisuellen Methode oder mit der Handpuppe (bei einigen Texten auch im Lehrer-Schüler-Dialog) gearbeitet werden;
- liefert Materialien zu einem handlungsbetonten Deutschunterricht, in dem Sprachstrukturen und Redemittel zum Ausdruck individueller kommunikativer Bedürfnisse schrittweise erarbeitet, gefestigt und erweitert werden. Eine Reihe kommunikativer Spiele (im Lehrerhandbuch) dient nicht nur der Auflockerung des Unterrichts, sondern auch der Übung sprachlicher Strukturen in kommunikativen Situationen;
- orientiert sich in Themen und Inhalten konsequent am Erfahrungsbereich der angesprochenen Altersgruppen: Band I = Schüler von 8-12 Jahren, Band II = Schüler von 9-14 Jahren, Band III = Schüler von 10-14 Jahren.
  So trägt die erste Stufe des Grundkurses nicht nur der Realität, sondern auch dem Spielbedürfnis und der Fantasie der Schüler Rechnung. Zugleich sollen die Schüler in den Texten und Bildern etwas erfahren über die deutschsprachigen Länder, insbesondere über die Lebensverhältnisse und Gewohnheiten Gleichaltriger in diesen Ländern. Der Grundkurs beschränkt sich dabei im wesentlichen auf die Bundesrepublik Deutschland;
- hat das Ziel, die Schüler in die deutsche Sprache einzuführen und ihnen Fertigkeiten und Kenntnisse zu vermitteln, die sie befähigen, sich in elementaren Situationen mündlich und schriftlich zu verständigen.
  Während die Übungen im **Schülerbuch** vor allem die mündliche Sprachbeherrschung schulen, zielt das **Arbeitsheft** besonders auf die Schulung der Schreibfertigkeit ab;
- gewährleistet nach Abschluß der zweiten Stufe einen unmittelbaren Übergang zu **Wer? Wie? Was? 3.**

Das **Lehrerhandbuch** bietet in einem allgemeinen Teil einen Überblick über Anlage und Zielsetzung des Lehrgangs sowie Erläuterungen zu den damit verbundenen methodisch-didaktischen Fragen. Der zweite Teil enthält konkrete Arbeitsvorschläge, die dem Lehrer die Gestaltung des Unterrichts erleichtern sollen.

Die Arbeit an diesem Band wurde beratend und organisatorisch begleitet von Walter Schmidt und Johann Westerhoff, beide Bundesverwaltungsamt - Zentralstelle für das Auslandsschulwesen - Köln. Ihnen schuldet der Verfasser besonderen Dank für Rat und Unterstützung bei der Konzeption, der Erstellung und der endgültigen Überarbeitung der Materialien.

Für kritische Hinweise ist u.a. zu danken: Werner Blieske (DS Lima), Peter Desmarets (Gesamthochschule Kassel), Walter Lohfert (Goethe-Institut München), Prof. G. Neuner (Gesamthochschule Kassel), Prof. H.-E. Piepho (Universität Gießen), Gunther Schneider (DS Valencia), Hermann Schuh (ZfA), H.-P. Wattler (DS Lima).

Bei der Arbeit an diesem Band hat der Verfasser wertvolle Anregungen erhalten aus Materialien von Bertold Feige (DS Barcelona), Werner Götz (DS Santa Cruz/Bolivien) und Hartmut Zeckai (DS La Paz).

Harald Seeger

Inhaltsverzeichnis

Nordsee
Ostsee
Hamburg
Rostock
Schwerin
Bremen
Lüneburg
Weser
Elbe
BERLIN
Oder
Hannover
Potsdam
Ems
Herford
Magdeburg
Rhein
Bielefeld
Goslar
Dortmund
Düsseldorf
Haan
Erfurt
Leipzig
Dresden
Neisse
D
Weimar
Köln
BONN
Chemnitz
Elbe
Frankfurt
Mosel
Offenbach
Main
Rhein
Neckar
Fürth
Nürnberg
Karlsruhe
Pforzheim
Stuttgart
Esslingen
Donau
Donau
München
Starnberg
Freiburg
Lörrach
Kempten
Rhein

Wo bist du?
Das ist ... .

1

Das ist Tanja.

Das ist Herr Müller.

-	Tanja!
o	Ja?

-	Wo bist du?
o	Hier. Ich bin hier.

Das ist	Tanja.
Das ist	Herr Müller.

Guten Tag! Ich bin ...

Ü = Übungen im Schülerbuch
AH = Übungen im Arbeitsheft
KS = Kommunikatives Spiel im Lehrerhandbuch (Teil III)

3

-	Guten Tag! Guten Tag, Kinder!	
o	Guten Tag, Guten Tag,	Herr Müller! Frau Adams!

Ich bin	Tanja.
Ich bin	Herr Müller.
Ich bin	Frau Adams.

$B_2 \rightarrow AH_1; B_3 \rightarrow AH_{2-3}$

LEKTION 1

C

Ich bin ....
Das ist ....
Bist du ...?

1

2

3

4

5

-	Ich bin Tanja. Und du?	
o	Ich bin	Susi. Petra. Thomas.

-	Bist du Anna?	
o	Ja.	
o	Nein, ich bin	Susi. Petra.

-	Das ist	Herr Müller. Susi.
o	Guten Tag,	Herr Müller! Susi!

-	Das ist Peter.	
o	Ja, das ist Peter.	
o	Nein, das ist	Hans. Thomas.

$C_5 \rightarrow AH_{4-6}$

D

Wir lernen Deutsch

E

Wo wohnst du?
Ich wohne in ... .
Wo wohnen Sie?

1

Wo wohnst du, Tanja?

Ich wohne in ... .

Und Sie? Wo wohnen Sie?

Ich wohne auch in ... .

2

Wo wohnst du, Susi?

In ... .

Und du, Peter?

Ich wohne auch in ... .

Ist das in Deutschland?

- Wo wohnst du, Petra?
o Ich wohne in Bonn.
- Und du, Thomas?
o Ich wohne auch in Bonn.

- Wo wohnen Sie, Herr Bott?
o Ich wohne in Bonn.
- Und Sie, Frau Liem?
o Ich wohne auch in Bonn.

$E_2 \rightarrow AH_{7-9}$

LEKTION 

F

Auf Wiedersehen!

-	Auf Wiedersehen! Auf Wiedersehen, Kinder!	
o	Auf Wiedersehen,	Tanja! Herr Müller! Frau Adams!

F → AH_{10}

Wir lesen 

Sigi und Sieglinde

Sigi! Siigi! Siiigi!
Ja?

Wo bist du, Sigi?
Hier. Ich bin hier.

Hallo, Sieglinde!
Hallo, Sigi! Das ist Waldi.

Guten Tag, Waldi!
Guten Tag, Sigi!

Wo wohnst du, Waldi?
WALDI
Ich wohne dort.

Und du, Sigi?
Ich wohne hier.

Ich auch.
Und du, Sieglinde?

Ja, wir wohnen hier.

LEKTION 1

Roboter
FAMILIE
ROBI

Guten Tag! Ich bin Tanja. Und du?
Guten Tag! Ich bin Robi eins.

Das ist Robi zwei, und das ist Robi drei.
Guten Tag, Kinder!

Lernst du Deutsch, Tanja?
Ja. Und du?

Ich lerne auch Deutsch.
DEUTSCH

Wir lernen Deutsch.

Auf Wiedersehen, Robi eins! Auf Wiedersehen, Kinder!
Auf Wiedersehen, Tanja!

Susi
Schlaksig

Guten Tag! Wohnen Sie hier?
Ja. Und du? Wo wohnst du?

Ich wohne auch hier.

Und wer bist du?
Ich bin Susi.

Und ich bin Herr Adams.

Auf Wiedersehen, Susi!
Auf Wiedersehen, Herr Adams!

KNACKER
GRAMMATIK
Knacker knackt jede Nuß!

1

Das ist	Tanja. Frau Adams. Herr Müller.

2

Ich wohne	in Bonn. in Hamburg. hier.

3

Ich	wohne hier.
Ich	lerne Deutsch.

Wir	wohnen hier.
Wir	lernen Deutsch.

Wohnst	du	auch hier?
Lernst	du	auch Deutsch?

Wohnen	Sie	auch hier?
Lernen	Sie	auch Deutsch?

4

Ich	bin	Susi.

Wir	sind	Hans und Peter.
Wir	sind	auch in Bonn.

	Bist	du	hier in Bonn?
Ja,	ich	bin	in Bonn.

5

-			Bist	du	Petra?
o	Ja,	ich	bin		Petra.
	Nein,	ich	bin		Susi.

-	Wo	bist	du?
o	Ich	bin	hier.
	Hier	bin	ich.

-	Wo	wohnst	du?
o	Ich	wohne	hier.

A

Setzt euch!
Setz dich!

⊕⊕

1

Setzt euch bitte, Kinder!

2

Setz dich bitte, Hans!

LEKTION 2

B

Wo ist ...?
... ist nicht hier.

⊕⊕

1

2

C

⊕⊕

Steh bitte auf!
Komm bitte!
Geh bitte raus!
Komm bitte rein!
Setz dich bitte!

$B_2 \rightarrow AH_1$

- Tanja,	steh bitte auf! komm bitte! geh bitte raus! komm bitte rein!	o Gut,	ich stehe auf. ich komme. ich gehe raus. ich komme rein.

- Geh bitte raus, Tanja!
  - o Wieso?
  - o Nein!
- Tanja, bitte!
  - o Gut, ich gehe raus.
  - o Nein!

C → AH_{2-5}

LEKTION 

Sag mal, wer ist das?

⊕⊕

1

Nein, Tanja. Falsch. Das ist Ulrich.

Ja, richtig! Das ist Ulrich.

2

VORNAMEN

Jungen	Mädchen
Ulrich	Stefanie
Michael	Ina
Peter	Jutta
Hans	Andrea
Klaus	Helga
Lutz.	Christina
Manfred	Birgit
Christian	Tanja
Hans-Peter	Monika
Karl-Heinz	Petra

FAMILIENNAMEN

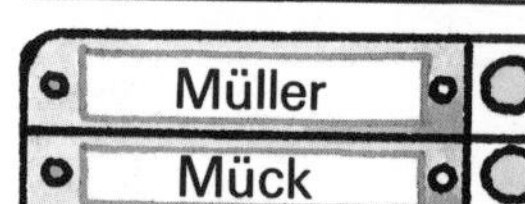

Müller
Mück
Liem
Schmidt
Fricke
Neumann
Scholz
Hilger
Schäfer
Meier

3

Was? Du bist nicht Ina? Wer bist du denn?

Ich bin Stefanie.

Ah, du bist Stefanie.

- Sag mal, wer ist das?
o Das ist ... .
- Ja, richtig. - Nein, falsch.

- Ich bin nicht Ina.
o Was? Du bist nicht Ina? Wer bist du denn?

D_3 → AH_6

4

Wer bin ich und wo wohne ich?

Beispiel:
- Scholz.
∘ Du bist Helga und wohnst in . . . .

$D_4 \rightarrow KS_1$

Wer bin ich?

- Sag mal, wer bin ich?

o Du bist … .

- Ja. Richtig. Richtig. Ja, ich bin … .	- Nein. Falsch. Falsch. Nein, ich bin nicht … .

E

Wie heißt du? Wie heißt dein ...?

⊕⊕

1

Heißt du Michael?
Ich? Ja, ich heiße Michael.

2

Und du heißt Heino?
Nein: Heiko, nicht Heino.

3

Heino:	**Ich** heiße Heino.
Petra:	Ach so, **du** bist Heino. Ist das dein Vater?
Heino:	Ja.
Petra:	Und wo ist deine Mutter?
Heino:	Meine Mutter ist dort.
Petra:	Ist das da dein Bruder?
Heino:	Ja. Und das ist meine Schwester.
Petra:	Wie heißt dein Bruder?
Heino:	Lutz.
Petra:	Und deine Schwester?
Heino:	Meine Schwester heißt Jutta.

- Heißt du ...?
- Du heißt ..., ja?

o Ja, (ich heiße) ... . o Nein, (ich heiße) ... .

- Wie heißt du?

o (Ich heiße) ... .

- Wie heißt dein Bruder?
  Wie heißt deine Schwester?

o Mein Bruder heißt ... .
  Meine Schwester heißt ... .

Wie heißt du?
Wie heißt dein Bruder?
Wie heißt deine Schwester?

$E_2 \rightarrow AH_7; E_3 \rightarrow KS_2$

LEKTION 

Wo bist du? Wer ist das? 

1

Heino: Wo bist du?
Petra: Hier. Das bin ich.

Heino: Was? Das bist du?
Petra: Ja.

Petra: Ist das dein Freund?
Heino: Ja, das ist mein bester Freund.

2

Petra: Und wie heißt dein Freund?
Heino: Jens.

Petra: Und wo bist du?
Heino: Ich bin nicht auf dem Bild.

3

Heino: Wer ist denn das da?
Petra: Das ist meine Freundin.
Heino: Deine beste Freundin?
Petra: Nein, jetzt nicht mehr.

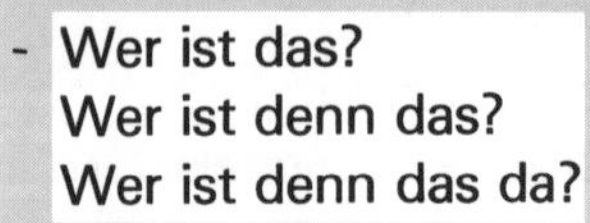

- Wer ist das?
  Wer ist denn das?
  Wer ist denn das da?

o Das bin ich.
  Das bist du.
  Das ist mein bester Freund.
  meine beste Freundin.

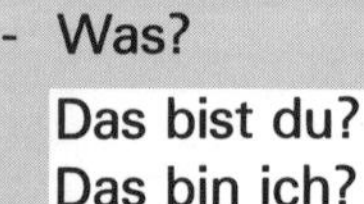

- Was?
  Das bist du?
  Das bin ich?
  Das ist dein Freund?
  deine Freundin?

$F_2 \rightarrow Ü_{1-2}; AH_8$

4

Lehrer: Wer ist auf dem Bild, Stefan?

Stefan:	Das ist	mein Bruder	meine Schwester
		Vater	Mutter
		Onkel	Tante
		Opa.	Oma.

Lehrer: Und wer ... ...?
Stefan: Das ist mein Freund.
Lehrer: Und wo bist ...?
Stefan: Hier. Das ... .
Lehrer: Ach ja, ... bist du.

- Wer ist auf dem Bild?
- Wer ist das (da)?

o Das ist ... .
o Das bin ich.

- Wo bist du auf dem Bild?

o Hier. Das bin ich.
- Ach ja, das bist du.

o Ich bin nicht auf dem Bild.
- Ach ja, du bist nicht auf dem Bild.

$F_4 \rightarrow Ü_{3-4}; AH_{9-11}$

LEKTION 

G

Meine Familie

⊕⊕

Mein Papa heißt Hans.
Mein Opa heißt Franz.
Meine Mama heißt Renate.
Meine Schwester heißt Beate.
Meine Oma heißt Ottilie.
Das ist meine Familie.
Ich heiße Fritz,
und mein Hund heißt Spitz.

H

Der Lehrer sagt

⊕⊕

1. Gruppe
1. Der Lehrer sagt: Wir singen jetzt. Kinder, kommt, wir
2. Gruppe
singen jetzt! Wir singen alle gern!

2. Der Lehrer sagt: Wir spielen jetzt. ... ...
3. Der Lehrer sagt: Wir lernen jetzt. ... ...

G → $AH_{1\,2}$

Wir lesen 

DACKEL
WALDI

Komm bitte raus!
Wir spielen.
WALDI

Wer bist
du denn?

Ich bin Pucki.
Und ich
heiße
Waldi.

Wau,wau

WALDI
Pucki, komm!
GRRR

Wer ist denn das?

Pst,
das ist
mein Onkel.
!

GRRR
GRRR

LEKTION 

Sigi und
Sieglinde

Wo bin ich?

Wer bin ich?

Ach, das bist du, Sieglinde.

Komm, steh auf, Sigi!

Setz dich bitte!

Roboter
FAMILIE
ROBI

Piep-Piep. Papa, Papa?

Ja. Komm rein und setz dich!

Hurra!
Papa?

Ja?

RAUS!

Susi Schlaksig

Guten Tag, Frau Schlaksig!

Wer bist du denn?
Das ist meine Freundin Petra.

Ah, du bist Petra?
Petra, komm rein!

Ist Opa hier?
Nein, Opa ist nicht hier.

Wer ist denn das auf dem Bild? Ist das dein Opa?

Nein, das bin ich.
Was? Du?

ÜBUNGEN 2

1 Wir fragen

Petra: ....?
Tanja: Das ist Herr Müller.

Petra: ....?
Tanja: Nein, ich bin nicht Sabine.

Petra: .... du denn?
Tanja: Ich bin Tanja.

Petra: Ah, du bist Tanja.
Tanja: Und du? ....?
Petra: Ich heiße Petra.

2 Heißt du Klaus Müller?

Hans: Hm. Klaus Müller.
Klaus Müller? Hallo! Du!
... du Klaus Müller?
Manfred: Nein. Ich ... Manfred Mück.

Hans: Und ...? ... du Klaus Müller?
Dirk: ..., ich ... nicht Klaus Müller. ... bin Dirk Lisch.

Hans: ... du? ... heißt du?
Peter: ...? Peter Bott.
Dort ist Klaus.

Klaus: Ich ... Klaus Müller.
... bist du?
Hans: Ich ... Hans Mann.
Hier bitte.

3 Familie Monster

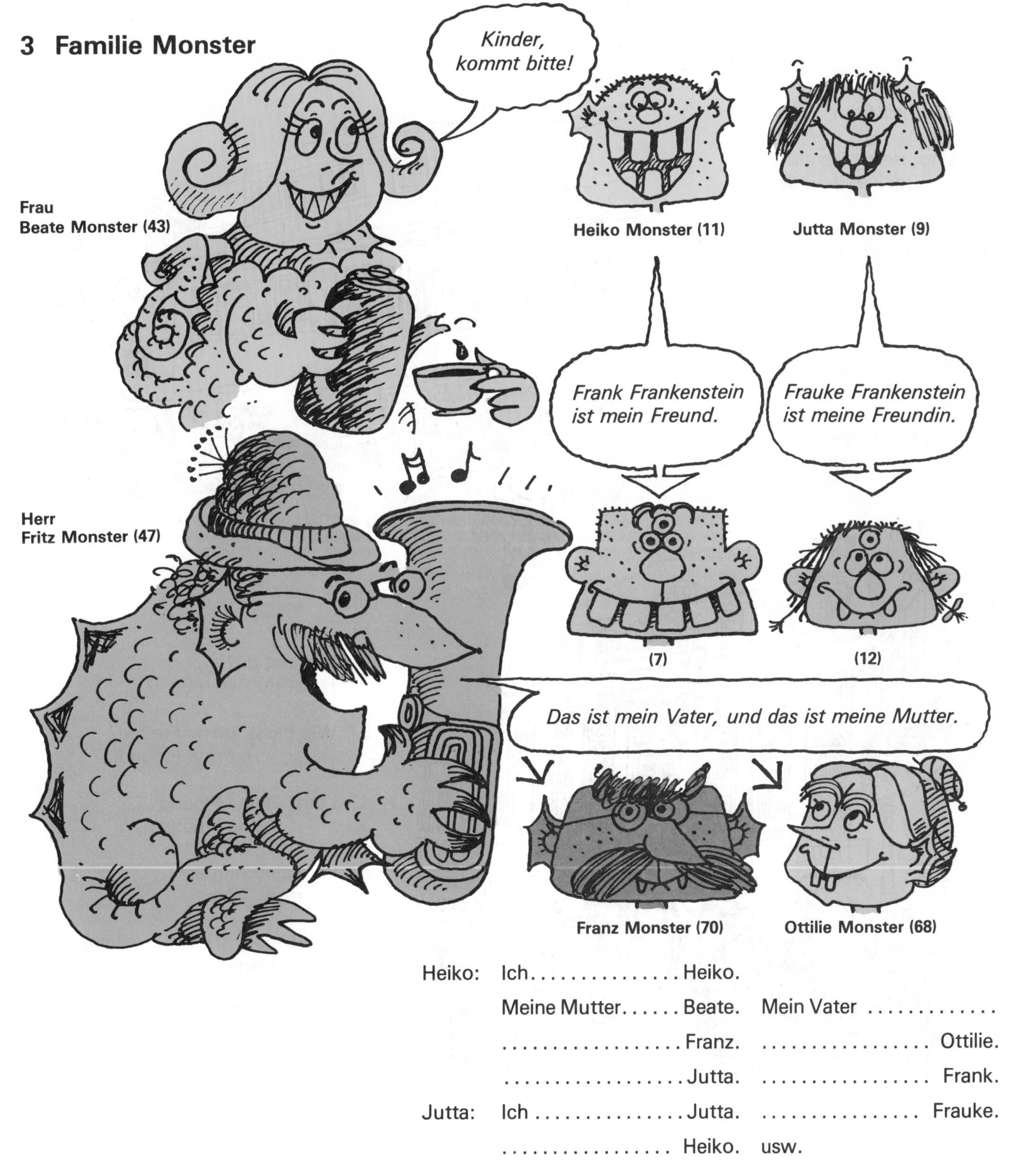

Heiko: Ich . . . . Heiko.
Meine Mutter . . . . . . Beate. Mein Vater . . . .
. . . . Franz. . . . . Ottilie.
. . . . Jutta. . . . . Frank.

Jutta: Ich . . . . Jutta. . . . . Frauke.
. . . . Heiko. usw.

Ich frage

Norbert Neugierig

Ich antworte

a)

1. Wie heißt du?
2. Und dein Freund? / deine Freundin?
3. Lernst du Deutsch?
4. Bist du hier auf dem Bild?
5. Ist das dein Vater? / deine Mutter?
6. Wer ist das da?
7. Ist Tanja deine Freundin?
8. Wie heißt dein Bruder? / deine Schwester?

b)

1. Wo bist du?
2. Heißt du Peter/Susi?
3. Wie heißt dein Freund? / deine Freundin?
4. Lernt dein Freund / deine Freundin Deutsch?
5. Ist deine Mutter / dein Vater hier?
6. Heißt dein Onkel / deine Tante Peter? / Ina?
7. Wie heißt dein Hund?
8. Bist du hier auf dem Bild?

KNACKER GRAMMATIK

Knacker knackt jede Nuß!

2

1 Ich bin .../ ich heiße ...; nein — nicht

	Du bist	Hans, ja?
Nein,	ich bin	nicht Hans.
	Ich bin	Peter.
	Das / Hier ist	Hans.

	Du heißt	Klaus, ja?
Nein,	ich heiße	nicht Klaus.
	Ich heiße	Peter.
	Mein Freund heißt	Klaus.

2 Das bin ich

	Das	bist du,	ja?
Nein,	das	bin ich	nicht.
Hier.	Das	bin ich.	
Was?	Das	bist du?	

3 Fragen und Antworten

Ich frage		Ich antworte
Heißt du Hans? Du heißt Hans, ja?		Ja, ich heiße Hans. Nein, ich heiße nicht Hans.
(Sag mal,)	wo ist Hans?	Hier ist Hans. Hans ist nicht hier.
(Sag mal,)	wer ist das? wer ist das auf dem Bild? wer bist du denn?	Das ist Peter. Das bin ich. Ich bin Hans.
(Sag mal,)	wie heißt du?	Ich heiße Hans.
(Sag mal,)	wie heißt dein Vater? wie heißt deine Mutter?	Mein Vater heißt Walter. Meine Mutter heißt Anna.

4

Du komm**st**.
lern**st** Deutsch.
spiel**st**.
sing**st**.
steh**st** auf.
geh**st** raus.
komm**st** rein.
heiß**t** Monika.

Ich komm**e**.
lern**e** Deutsch.
spiel**e**.
sing**e**.
steh**e** auf.
geh**e** raus.
komm**e** rein.
heiß**e** Dirk.

Sie komm**en**.
lern**en** Deutsch.
spiel**en**.
sing**en**.
steh**en** auf.
geh**en** raus.
komm**en** rein.
heiß**en** Müller.

Wir komm**en**.
lern**en** Deutsch.
spiel**en**.
sing**en**.
steh**en** auf.
geh**en** raus.
komm**en** rein.
heiß**en** Dirk und Anna.

5 mein-meine/dein-deine

Das ist mein / dein
- Bruder
- Vater
- Onkel
- Opa
- Freund

Das ist meine / deine
- Schwester
- Mutter
- Tante
- Oma
- Freundin

6 Das hörst du in der Schule

1

2

3

4

5

6

7

8

LEKTION 

Was machst du?
Sag mal, wie heißt ... auf deutsch?

1

Hier Tanja.

Hallo, Tanja! Hier ist Paul!

Tag, Paul! Was machst du?

Ich mache Deutsch-Hausaufgaben. Und du?

Ich auch. Ich mache auch Deutsch.

2

Sag mal, wie heißt auf deutsch?

? Haus.

Noch einmal, bitte!

Haus.

Danke, Tanja. Und ?

Heft.

Danke, Tanja. Auf Wiedersehen!

Auf Wiedersehen, Paul!

- Hier Tanja.
o Hallo, Tanja. Hier ist Paul.
- Tag, Paul.

- Was machst du?
o Ich mache Hausaufgaben.
Ich mache Deutsch.

- Sag mal, wie heißt auf deutsch?
o Haus.
- Noch einmal, bitte!
o Haus.
- Danke.

$A_1 \rightarrow AH_1; A_2 \rightarrow Ü_1$

B

Wie heißt das auf deutsch?
Füller. Das ist ein Füller.

1

Wie heißt das auf deutsch?
Füller. Das ist ein Füller.
Ach so. Das ist ein Füller. Danke.

Ebenso mit:

1
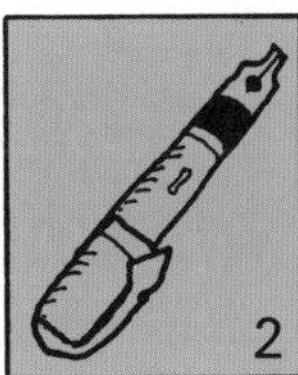
2

3
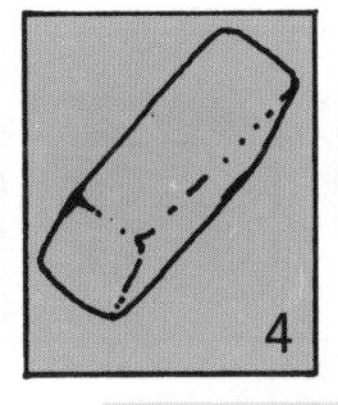
4
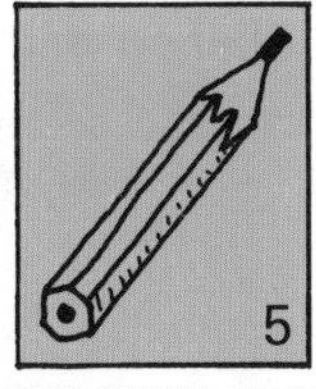
5

6

- Wie heißt das auf deutsch?
o Füller.
  Füller. Das ist ein Füller.
- Ach so. Das ist ein Füller.
  Danke.

2 Das ist ein … .

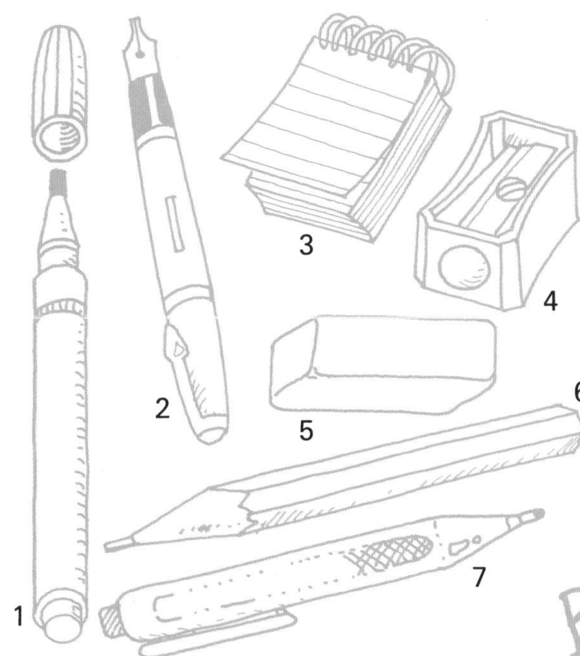
1
2
3
4
5
6
7

Block
Kuli
Radiergummi
Füller
Filzstift
Spitzer
Bleistift

$B_2 \rightarrow Ü_2$;AH_{2-3}

Wie heißt das auf deutsch?
Tafel. Das ist eine Tafel.

1

Wie heißt das auf deutsch?
Ich weiß es nicht. Frag Peter!
Peter, wie heißt das auf deutsch?
Tafel.
Natürlich. Das ist eine Tafel.

Ebenso mit:

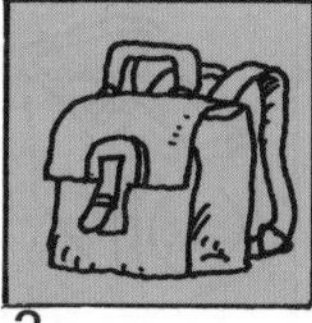

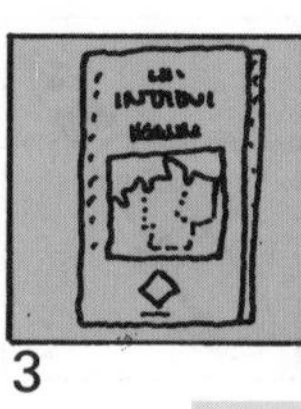

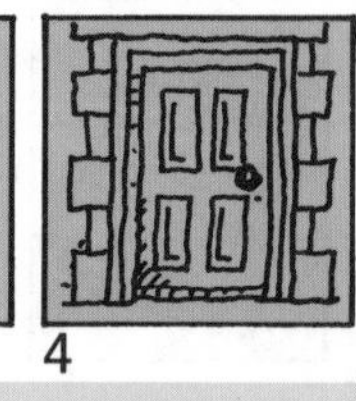

1 2 3 4 5 6

- Wie heißt das auf deutsch?
o Ich weiß es nicht. o Das ist ...

2 Das ist eine ... .

$C_2 \rightarrow Ü_3$

Wie heißt das auf deutsch?
Buch. Das ist ein Buch.

1

Julia, wie heißt das auf deutsch?
Buch!
Wie bitte?
Buch.
Ach so. Das ist ein Buch.
1
2
3
4

Ebenso mit:

- Wie heißt das auf deutsch?
o Buch.
- Wie bitte?
o Buch.
Das ist ein Buch.

2 Das ist ein .... .

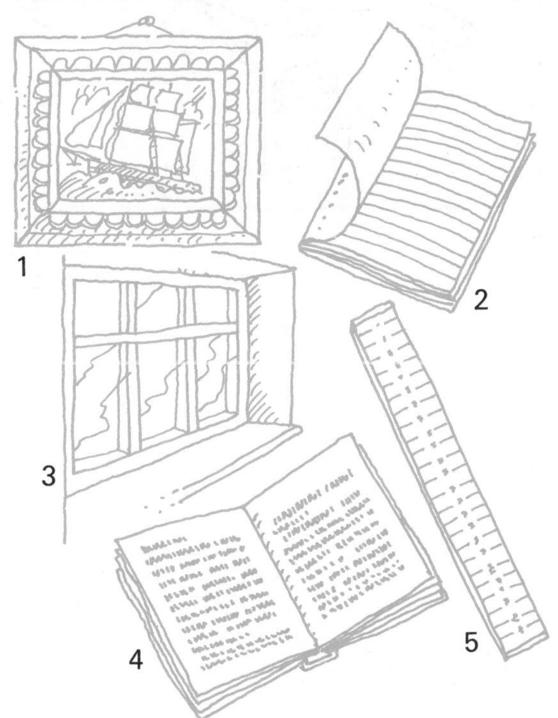

Heft
Fenster
Lineal
Buch
Bild

$D_2 \rightarrow Ü_{4,6}$; AH_{4-8}

LEKTION 

3 Wie heißt das auf deutsch?

Das ist ein ...

Das ist ein ...

Das ist eine ...

- Sag mal, wie heißt das auf deutsch?

o Buch.

o Ich weiß es nicht.
- Frag Peter!

o Peter, wie heißt ...?

- Noch einmal, bitte.
  Wie bitte?

o Buch.
  Das ist ein Buch.

- Natürlich. Das ist ein Buch.
  Ach so, das ist ein Buch.
  Danke.

$D_3 \rightarrow Ü_{5,8}; AH_{9,11}$

E

Eins, **zwei**, Polizei.

Drei, **vier**, Offizier.

Fünf, **sechs**, alte Hex.

Sieben, **acht**, gute Nacht!

Neun, **zehn**. Auf Wieder**sehen**!

F

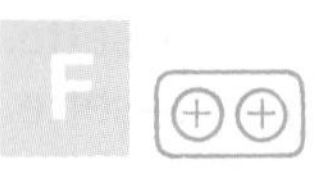

Bruder Jakob

die Glocken (Pl.)

1.
Bruder Jakob, Bruder Jakob,
2.
schläfst du noch? Schläfst du noch?
3.
Hörst du nicht die Glocken? Hörst du nicht die Glocken?
4.
Bim, bam, bum. Bim, bam, bum.

F → Ü7

LEKTION 

G

Das ist der ... .
das ... .
die ... .

1

Sag mal, Susi, ist das dein Bleistift?

Nein, das ist der Bleistift von Hans.

Sag mal, Petra, ist das dein Lineal?

Nein, das ist das Lineal von Susi.

Sag mal, Julia, ist das deine Kassette?

Nein, das ist die Kassette von Ulrich.

Das ist **ein** Bleistift.
Das ist **mein** Bleistift.
Das ist **der** Bleistift von Hans.

Das ist **ein** Lineal.
Das ist **mein** Lineal.
Das ist **das** Lineal von Susi.

Das ist **eine** Kassette.
Das ist **meine** Kassette.
Das ist **die** Kassette von Ulrich.

2

Das ist der Bleistift von Hans.
Das ist das Lineal von ...
Das ist ... ...

$G_2 \rightarrow AH_{10}$

Wir lesen 

DACKEL
WALDI

Wer ist denn das?
Ich weiß es nicht.

Das ist meine Familie.
Wie bitte?

Susi
Schlaksig
Hallo, Robi 3!
Hier ist Susi.

Was machst du?
Ich spiele.
Und du?

Ich mache Deutsch.

Sag mal, wie heißt
auf deutsch?
Und ?

Stuhl · Tisch · Lampe · Tür

Danke.
Stuhl
Tisch
Lampe
Tür

Sag mal, Susi,
schläfst du?

Natürlich nicht.
Ich mache Hausaufgaben.
Stuhl
Tisch
Lampe
Tür

Ach so.
Du machst Hausaufgaben.

1 Wir telefonieren (Du bist Paul oder Tanja.)

2 Wir spielen das Telefongespräch noch einmal mit:

3 Ebenso mit:

4 Ebenso mit:

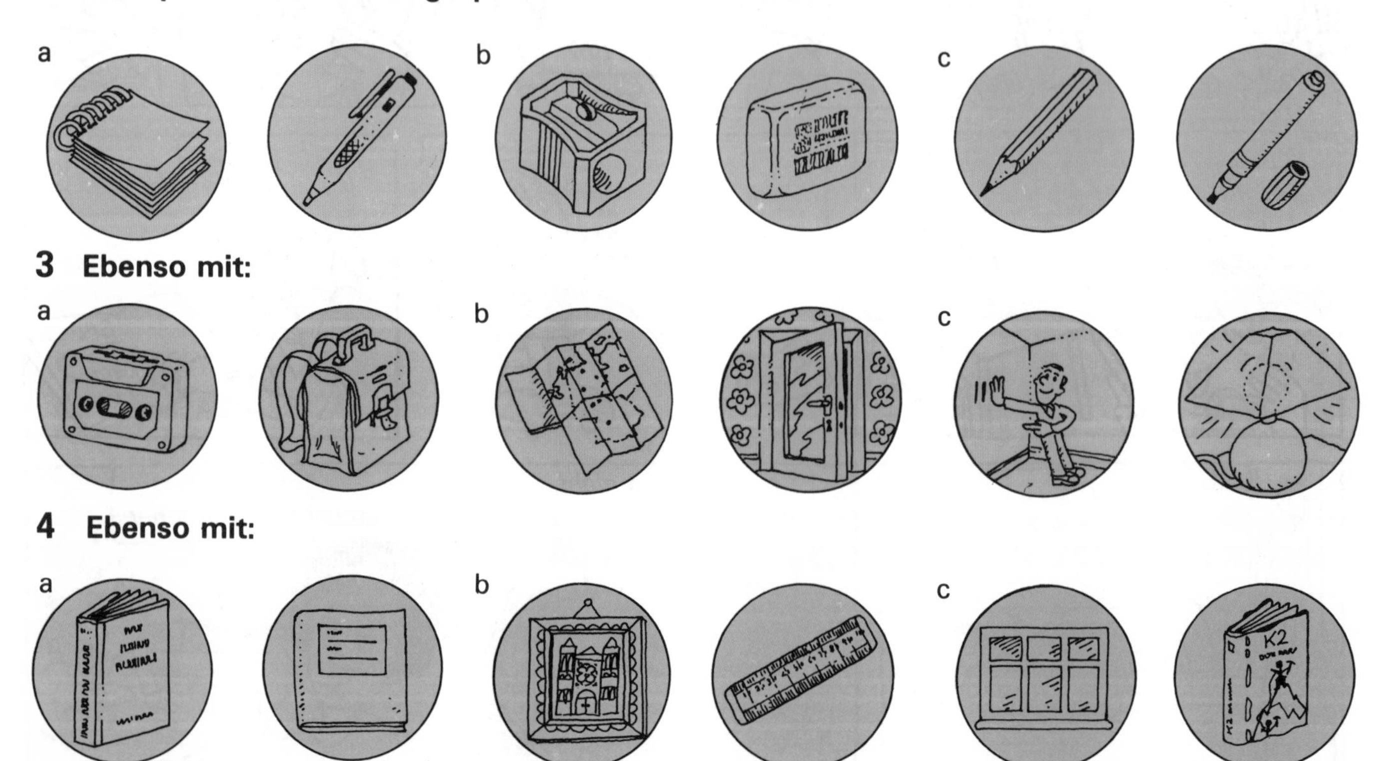

5 Wir sprechen

Haus - Heft - hier - heiße - Heiko - Hanna - hallo - Hund
ich - euch - nicht - dich - Ulrich - richtig
ach ja - ach so - Buch - noch einmal - auch - mache - machst
Tisch - Tasche - Schreibmaschine
Bleistift - Filzstift - steh auf - Spitzer
Füller - Müller - Mück - fünf
Tür - natürlich

Hallo Heiko!
Hier ist dein Heft.
Ich mache hier Hausaufgaben.
Und du? Ich auch.
Ich heiße Ulrich.
Ich heiße auch Ulrich.
Ulrich, ist das deine Tasche?
Natürlich, das ist meine Tasche.

6 Wir sprechen die Rollen von Paul, Tanja und Julia

1 
Wie heißt das auf deutsch?

2 
Ich weiß es nicht. Frag Julia!

3 
Wie heißt das auf deutsch?

4 
....

5 
Wie bitte?

6 
Das ist ein/eine ....

7 
Ach so.
Das ist ein/eine ....

8 

a

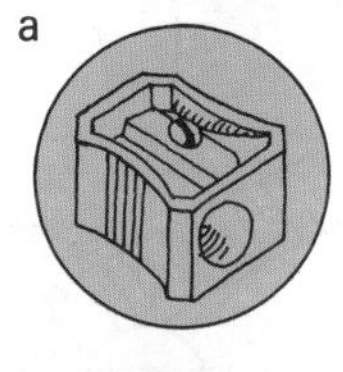 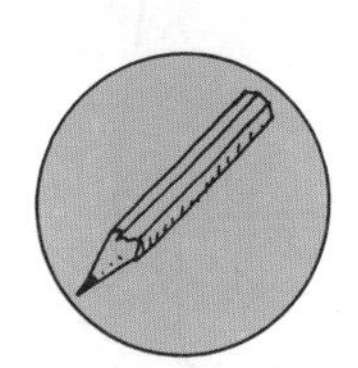 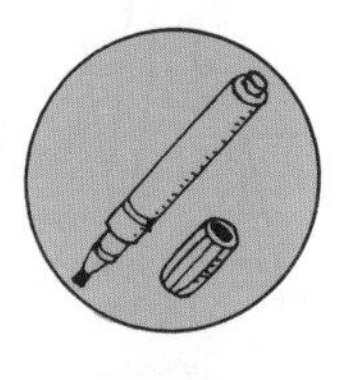   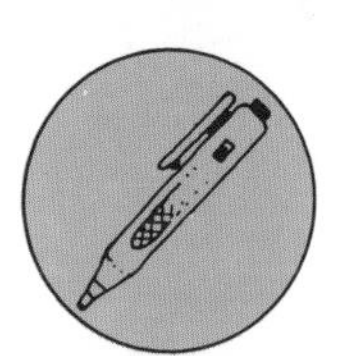

b

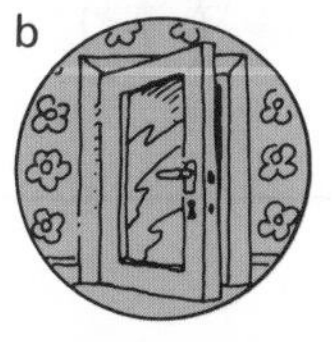   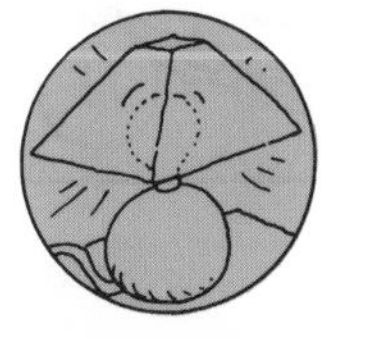  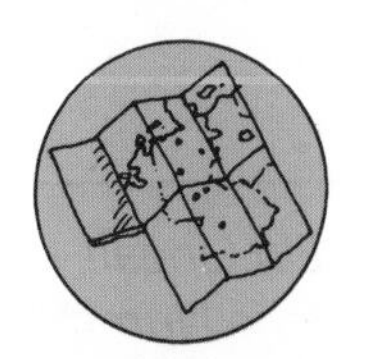

c

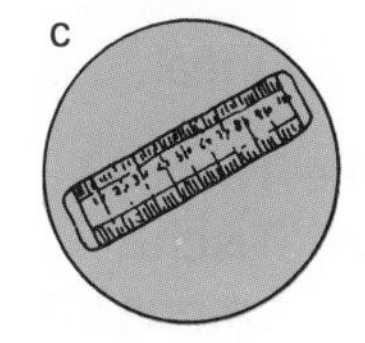     

7

Ein Lineal! Welche Nummer ist das?

Beispiel: - Ist Nummer 7 ein Bleistift? o Nein. Das ist ein Lineal.

Ist Nummer 6 ein Buch?
Ist Nummer 5 ein Heft?
Ist Nummer 3 ein Stuhl?

Ist Nummer 4 eine Tasche?
Ist Nummer 9 ein Tisch?
Ist Nummer 10 eine Lampe? usw.

8

Nina und Norbert Neugierig

a)

1. Wie heißt du?
2. Wohnst du hier?
3. Machst du hier Hausaufgaben?
4. Ist das dein Heft?
5. Sag mal, wie heißt auf deutsch?
6. Und ? Und ?
7. Wie heißt das auf deutsch?
8. Abrakadabra.

b)

1. Wer bist du?
2. Heißt dein | Freund | Frank?
deine | Freundin | Frauke?
3. Lernst du Deutsch?
4. Sag mal, wie heißt das auf deutsch?
5. Und das ?
6. Wie bitte?
7. Noch einmal, bitte.

   Ach so, Radiergummi.

3

KNACKER
GRAMMATIK
Knacker knackt jede Nuß!

1 Was machst du?

o Ich | singe / mache Hausaufgaben.

2 Wie heißt das auf deutsch?

o Füller. / Heft. / Lampe.

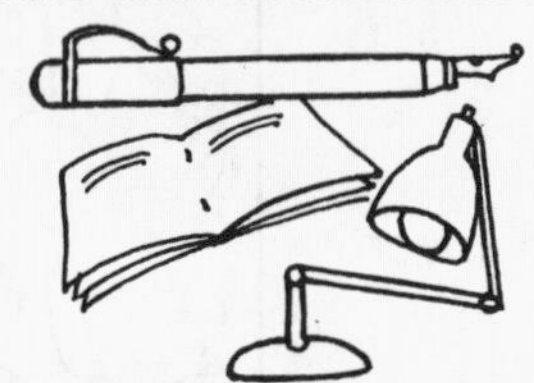

3 Das ist

	ein	mein / dein	
der	Füller, Bleistift, Block, Stuhl, Kuli, Radiergummi, Spitzer, Filzstift, Tisch		*von Hans*

	ein	mein / dein	
das	Buch, Telefon, Fenster, Heft, Bild, Lineal		*von Frau Adams*

	eine	meine / deine	
die	Tür, Tafel, Landkarte, Kassette, Tasche, Lampe, Puppe, Schreibmaschine		*von Monika*

4 Zahlen

1	2	3	4	5	6	7	8	9	10
eins	zwei	drei	vier	fünf	sechs	sieben	acht	neun	zehn
I	II	III	IIII	~~IIII~~	~~IIII~~ I	~~IIII~~ II	~~IIII~~ III	~~IIII~~ IIII	~~IIII~~ ~~IIII~~

Die Woche

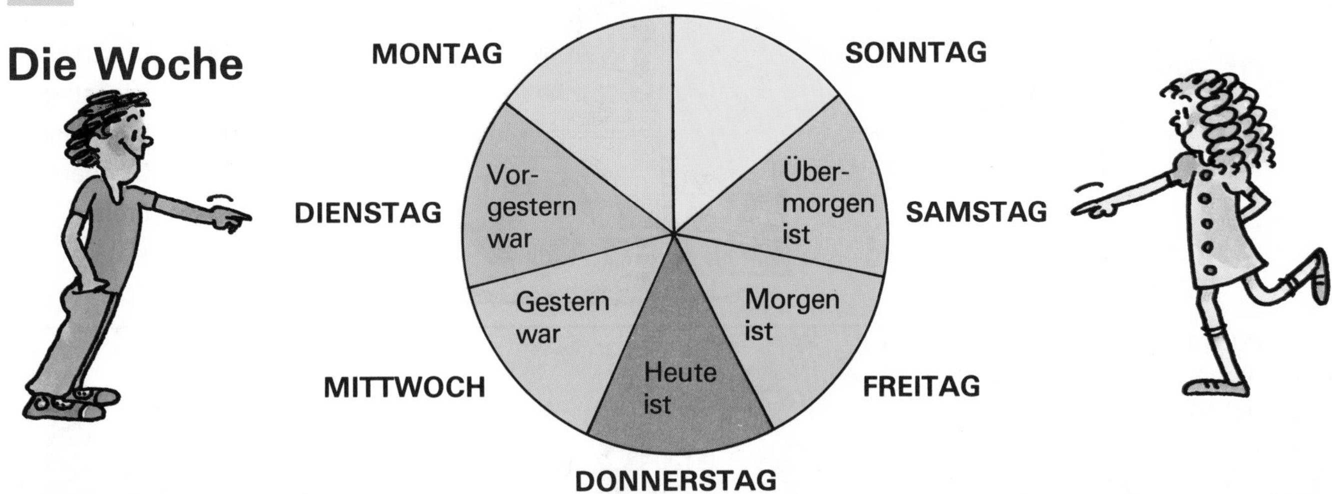

Ist heute Montag/Dienstag/.../...?	Ja, heute **ist** Montag/Dienstag/... . Nein, heute **ist** nicht Montag/... . Nein, heute **ist** Mittwoch/... .
Ist [morgen / übermorgen] Mittwoch/Donnerstag/...?	Ja, [morgen / übermorgen] **ist** Mittwoch/... . Nein, [morgen / übermorgen] **ist** nicht Mittwoch/... . Nein, [morgen / übermorgen] **ist** Freitag/... .
War [gestern / vorgestern] Sonntag/Montag/...?	Ja, [gestern / vorgestern] **war** Sonntag/... . Nein, [gestern / vorgestern] **war** nicht Sonntag/... . Nein, [gestern / vorgestern] **war** Donnerstag/... .
Welcher Tag **ist** [heute? / morgen? / übermorgen?] Welcher Tag **war** [gestern? / vorgestern?]	[Heute / Morgen / Übermorgen] **ist** ... [Gestern / Vorgestern] **war** ....

A → AH 1-5

B

Wann war/ist Fritz Mück in ...?

Mo	=	Montag
Di	=	Dienstag
Mi	=	Mittwoch
Do	=	Donnerstag
Fr	=	Freitag

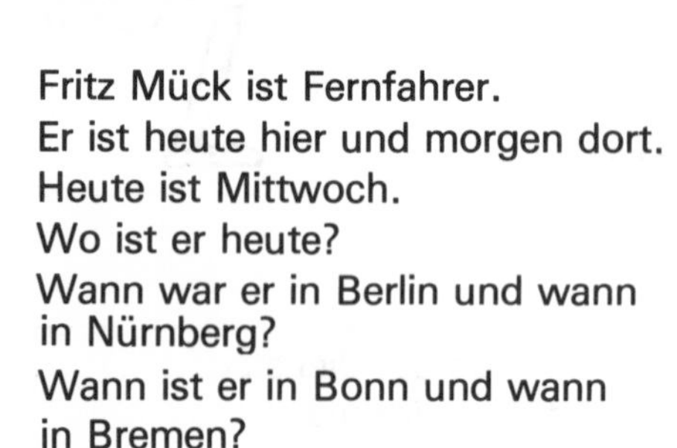

Fritz Mück ist Fernfahrer.
Er ist heute hier und morgen dort.
Heute ist Mittwoch.
Wo ist er heute?
Wann war er in Berlin und wann in Nürnberg?
Wann ist er in Bonn und wann in Bremen?

Berlin (Mo)

Bremen (Di)

Bonn (Mi)

Frankfurt (Do)

Nürnberg (Fr)

-	**Wann war**		Fritz Mück	in Bremen
o	Er	**war**	gestern am Dienstag	in Bremen.

-	**Wann ist**		er	in Bonn?
o	Er	**ist**	heute	in Bonn.

-	**Wann ist**		er	in Nürnberg?
o	Er	**ist**	übermorgen am Freitag	in Nürnberg.

-	**Wo war**	er	am Montag?	
o	Er	**war**	am Montag	in Berlin.

B → AH_8

C

Zu Hause, nach Hause, bei Petra, zu Petra

Ich bin

zu Hause

Ich gehe

nach Hause

- Wo warst du gestern? o Ich **war zu Hause.**	- Was machst du jetzt? o Ich **gehe nach Hause.**

1

Wo warst du gestern, Susi?
Ich war zu Hause.

Und du?
Ich war auch zu Hause.

2

Was machst du jetzt?
Ich gehe nach Hause.

Und du?
Ich auch.

LEKTION 

3

Susi *ist* **bei** Petra.

Tanja *geht* auch **zu** Petra.

Guten Tag, Tanja!
Guten Tag, Frau Liem! Ist Susi hier?

Nein, Susi ist bei Petra.
Gut, dann gehe ich auch zu Petra.

- Ist Susi hier?
o Nein, Susi **ist bei** Petra.

- Was machst du?
o Ich **gehe zu** Petra.

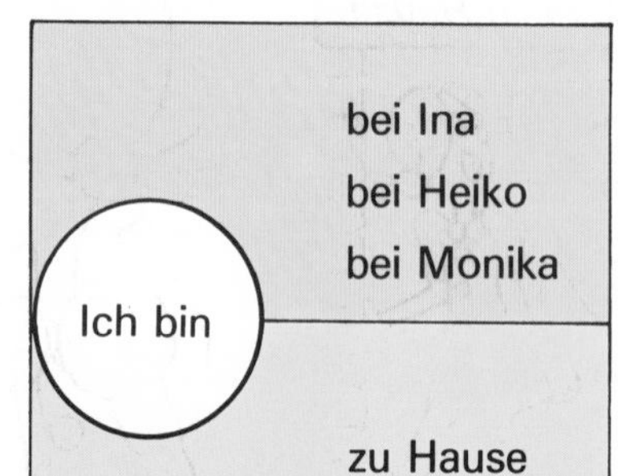

bei Ina
bei Heiko
bei Monika
Ich bin
zu Hause

Ich gehe

zu Ina
zu Heiko
zu Monika

nach Hause

$C_3 \rightarrow Ü_{1-3}; AH_{6,7,9-10}; KS_3$

Wir lesen

1

Klingeling!

Ja, Waldi ist zu Hause.
Waldi, komm! Telefon!

2

Warst du das?

Nein, das war ich nicht.
Das war Waldi.

3

MIAU ... MIAU!
Komm, ich bin
dein Freund.

1

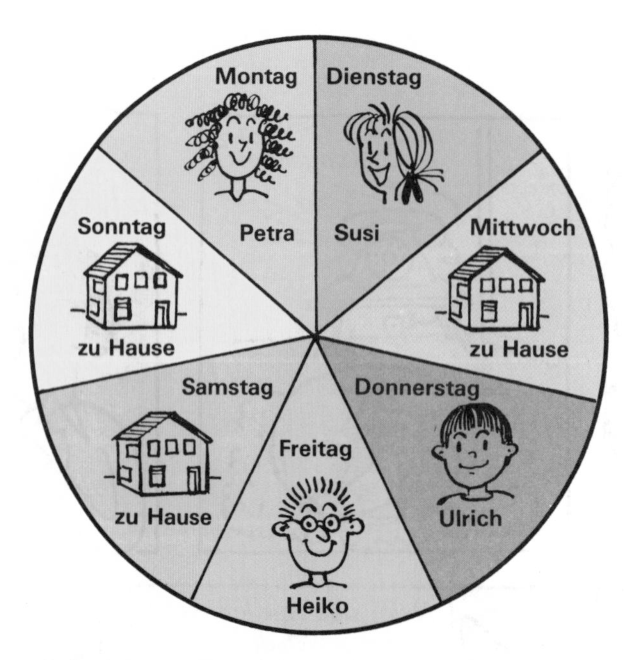

Beispiel:
- Tanja, wo warst du am Samstag?
o Ich war **zu Hause**.
- Wo warst du am Montag?
o Ich war **bei** Petra. usw.

2

Beispiel:
- Tanja, gehst du nach Hause?
o 1. Ja, ich gehe **nach Hause**.
o 2. Nein, ich gehe **zu** Petra.

3

a)
1. Ist deine Mutter heute zu Hause?
2. Dein Vater auch?
3. Ist dein Vater Fernfahrer?
4. Wie heißt dein Freund? / deine Freundin?
5. Warst du heute bei ...?
6. Gehst du morgen zu ...?
7. Wo machst du Hausaufgaben?
8. Ist morgen Dienstag?
9. Welcher Tag war gestern?

b)
1. Hallo, ist das deine Landkarte?
2. Wie heißt du?
3. Ist das dein Vater?
4. Und wer ist das da?
5. Warst du in Köln?
6. Wo wohnst du?
7. Wie bitte?
8. Fährst du jetzt nach Hause?

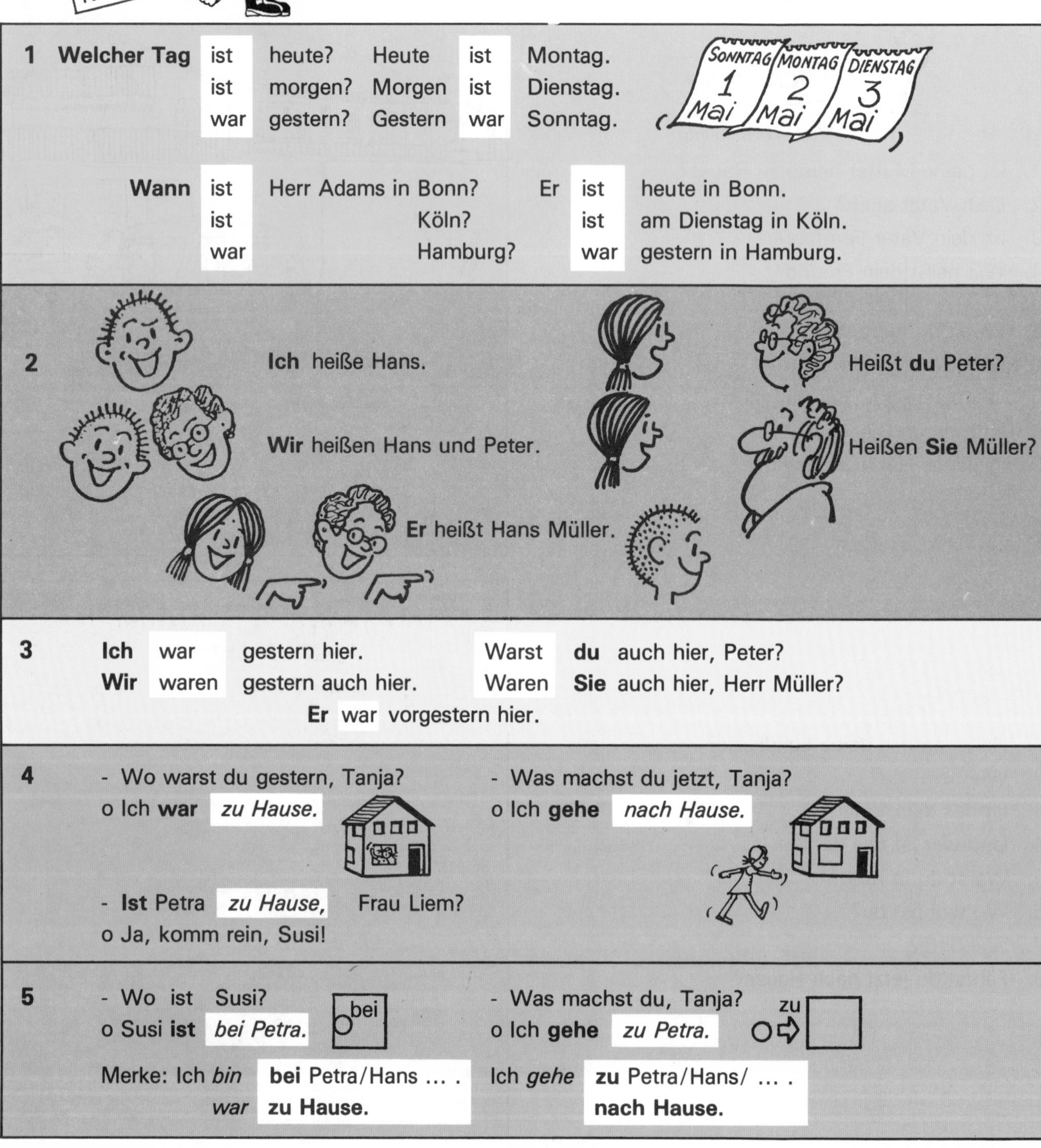

1

Welcher Tag	ist	heute?	Heute	ist	Montag.
	ist	morgen?	Morgen	ist	Dienstag.
	war	gestern?	Gestern	war	Sonntag.

Wann	ist	Herr Adams in Bonn?	Er	ist	heute in Bonn.
	ist	Köln?		ist	am Dienstag in Köln.
	war	Hamburg?		war	gestern in Hamburg.

2

Ich heiße Hans.

Wir heißen Hans und Peter.

Er heißt Hans Müller.

Heißt **du** Peter?

Heißen **Sie** Müller?

3

Ich	war	gestern hier.	Warst	**du**	auch hier, Peter?
Wir	waren	gestern auch hier.	Waren	**Sie**	auch hier, Herr Müller?

Er war vorgestern hier.

4

- Wo warst du gestern, Tanja?
o Ich **war** *zu Hause.*

- Was machst du jetzt, Tanja?
o Ich **gehe** *nach Hause.*

- **Ist** Petra *zu Hause,* Frau Liem?
o Ja, komm rein, Susi!

5

- Wo ist Susi?
o Susi **ist** *bei Petra.*

- Was machst du, Tanja?
o Ich **gehe** *zu Petra.*

Merke: Ich *bin* / *war* **bei** Petra/Hans … . / **zu Hause.**

Ich *gehe* **zu** Petra/Hans/ … . / **nach Hause.**

A

Was macht Peter am Montag/ am Dienstag/ ...?

1

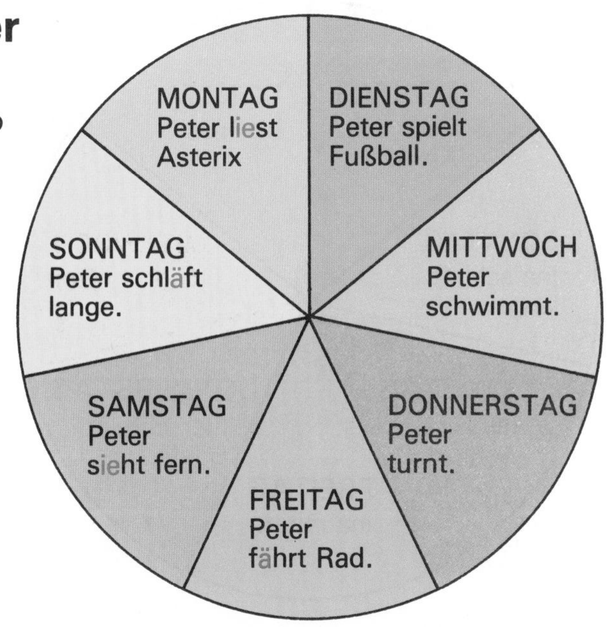

Peter liest Asterix

Peter spielt Fußball.

Peter schwimmt.

Peter turnt.

Peter fährt Rad.

Peter sieht fern.

Peter schläft lange.

2

Ich sehe auch fern.

Ich lese auch Asterix.

1. Heute ist Montag.
Was macht er heute? - Er ... .
Was machst du heute, Peter? - Ich ... .

2. Heute ist ... .
Was macht er heute? - Er ... .
Was machst du heute, Peter? - Ich ... .

Ich spiele auch Fußball.
Ich fahre auch Rad.

3. Heute ist ... .
Was macht er heute? - Er ... .
Was machst du heute, Peter? - Ich ... .

4. Heute ist ... .
Was macht er heute? - Er ... .
Was machst du heute, Peter? - Ich ... .

5. Heute ist ... .
Was macht er heute? - Er ... .
Was machst du heute, Peter? - Ich ... .

Ich schwimme auch.
Ich turne auch.

6. Heute ist ... .
Was macht er heute? - Er ... .
Was machst du heute, Peter? - Ich ... .

7. Heute ist ... .
Was macht er heute? - Er ... .
Was machst du heute, Peter? - Ich ... .

Ich schlafe auch lange.

$A_2 \rightarrow AH_{1-3}$

LEKTION 

B

Was macht Ina am Montag/ am Dienstag/. . .?

1

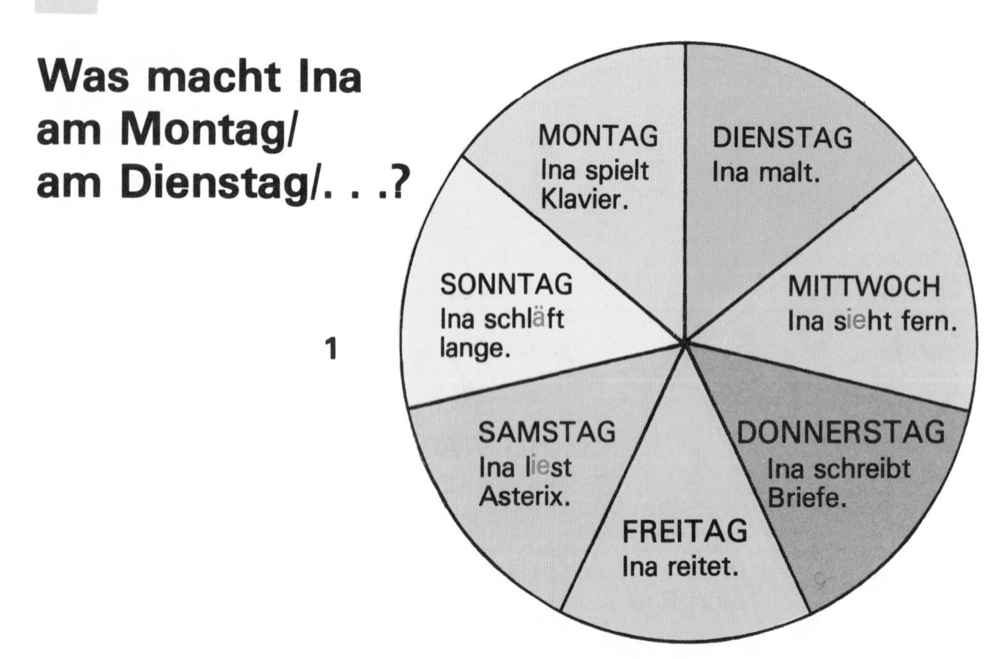

Ina sieht fern.

Ina schreibt Briefe.

Ina reitet.

Ina liest Asterix.

Ina schläft lange.

2

Ich schreibe auch Briefe.

1. Heute ist Montag.
Was macht Ina? Sie . . .
Was machst du heute, Ina? Ich . . .

Ich reite auch.

5. Heute ist . . .
ASTERIX
Was macht Ina? Sie . . .
Was machst du heute Ina? Ich . . .

Ich male auch.

7. Heute ist . . .
ZZZZ
Was macht Ina? Sie . . .
Was machst du heute, Ina? Ich.

3

Was fehlt?

Mittwoch.

Susi: *Hallo, Ina. Was ... ... ?*
Ina: *Ich ... .*
Susi: *Dein Bruder auch?*
Ina: *Nein, er ... .*

Samstag

Klaus: *Hallo, Peter. Was ... ... ?*
Peter: *Ich ... .*
Klaus: *... ... ... ?*
Peter: *Nein, sie ... .*

Freitag

Klaus: *Hallo, Peter. Was ... ... ?*
Peter: *Ich fahre Rad.*
Klaus: *... ... ... ?*
Peter: *Nein, sie ... .*

Beispiel: **Montag.**

Klaus: *Hallo, Peter. Was machst du?*
Peter: *Ich lese Asterix.*
Klaus: *Deine Schwester auch?*
Peter: *Nein, sie spielt Klavier.*

Donnerstag

Susi: *Hallo, Ina. Was ... ... ?*
Ina: *Ich ... .*
Susi: *... ... ... ?*
Ina: *Nein, er ... .*

Dienstag

Susi: *Hallo, Ina. Was ... ... ?*
Ina: *Ich ... .*
Susi: *... ... ... ?*
Ina: *Nein, er ... .*

$B_3 \rightarrow AH_{4-5}; KS_{4-5}$

C

Meine Woche

ich fahr'	=	ich fahre
ich seh'	=	ich sehe
ich spiel'	=	ich spiele
ich schlaf'	=	ich schlafe
ich hör'	=	ich höre

Am **Montag** fahr' ich Fahrrad.
Am **Dienstag** seh' ich fern.
Am **Mittwoch** spiel' ich Fußball.
Das mach' ich sehr, sehr gern.
Am **Donnerstag**, da schwimmen wir.
Am **Freitag** spiele ich Klavier.
Am **Samstag** kommt Frau Stange.
Am **Sonntag** schlaf' ich lange.
Und schon hör' ich die Mama:
"Komm, Peter! Steh auf! Schule!"
Ja, dann ist der **Montag** da.

D

Was machst du gern/lieber/am liebsten?

1

gern

lieber

am liebsten

C → KS_6

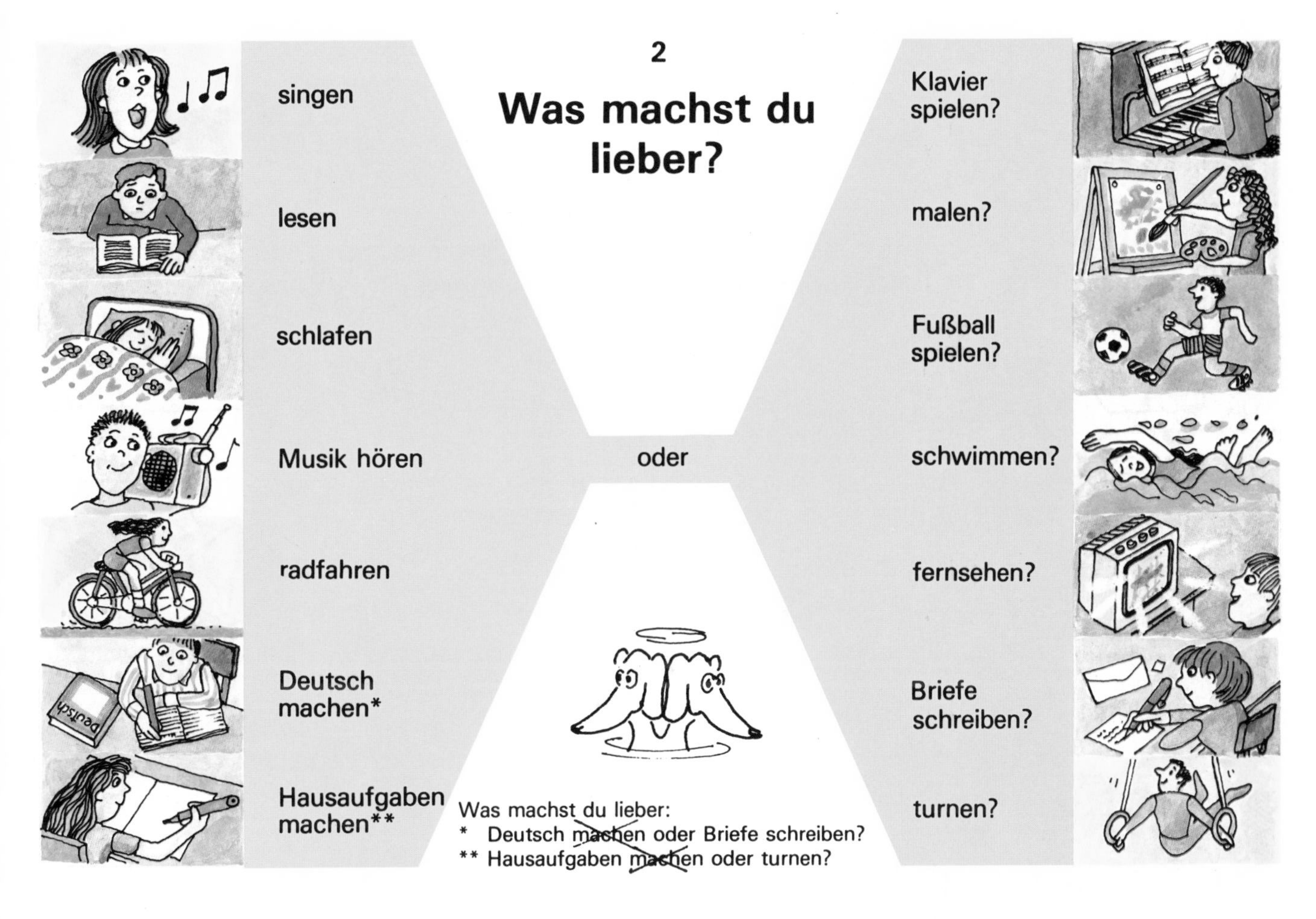

Was macht dein Bruder/deine Schwester
dein Freund/deine Freundin/dein Vater/
deine Mutter **gern**?
Was nicht?

- Was machst du **am liebsten**?

o Ich	turne	am liebsten	.—
	fahre		Rad.
	sehe		fern.
	spiele		Fußball.
	schreibe		Briefe.
	spiele		Klavier.

- Was machst du **lieber**: Fußball spielen oder radfahren?
o Ich fahre lieber Rad.

o Was machst du **gern**?
- Ich schwimme gern.

- Was machst du **nicht gern**?
o Ich spiele nicht gern Klavier.

$D_2 \rightarrow Ü_1$;AH_{6-10}

LEKTION 

Wir lesen 

Nero, sag mal, was machst du gern?

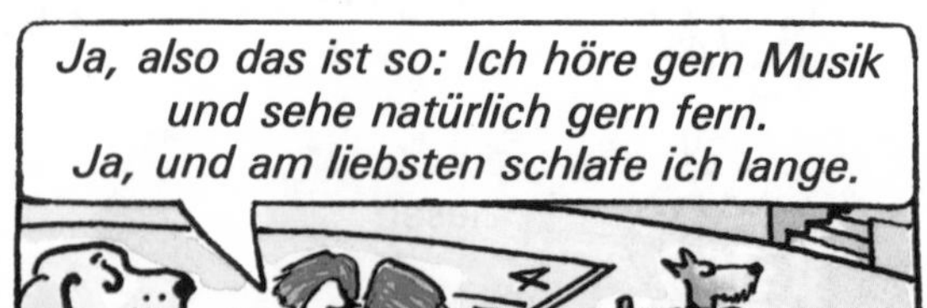

Ja, also das ist so: Ich höre gern Musik und sehe natürlich gern fern. Ja, und am liebsten schlafe ich lange.

Und du, Waldi?
Ich schwimme gern und turne gern und fahre am liebsten Rad.

Jetzt fahre ich auch Rad!

Wann kommt Tante Frieda?

Hier ist ein Stuhl!
Setz dich!

Nein! Wir haben viel Arbeit!

Was machst du denn hier?

Ich sage: Raus!

Wer spielt denn da Klavier?

Du siehst zu viel fern.

Was liest du denn da?
Asterix! Na so was!
ASTERIX

Ich gehe lieber.
Ich auch.

Komm! Wir haben viel Arbeit.

So ist es gut.
Brav!

Sag mal, Sieglinde,
wann fährt Tante Frieda
wieder nach Hause?

ÜBUNGEN 5

1

Nina und Norbert Neugierig

a)

1. Sag mal, ist heute Donnerstag?
2. Lernst du Deutsch?
3. Wann machst du Deutsch?
4. Wie heißt dein Lehrer?
5. Machst du gern Deutsch?
6. Machst du auch gern Hausaufgaben?
7. Was machst du am liebsten?
8. Ist das dein Bus?

b)

1. Ist dein Freund / deine Freundin auch hier?
2. Wie heißt er? / sie?
3. Liest dein Freund / deine Freundin gern Asterix?
4. Und deine Oma?
5. Wo liest dein Freund / deine Freundin Asterix:
   hier oder zu Hause?

GRAMMATIK
KNACKER
Knacker knackt jede Nuß!
5

1

Ich male
turne
schwimme
spiele
lese
heiße Dirk.
schlafe lange.
fahre Rad.
sehe fern.

Du
Malst du auch?
Turnst du auch?
Schwimmst du auch?
Spielst du auch?
Liest (!) du auch?
Heißt (!) du Lutz?
Schläfst du auch lange?
Fährst du auch Rad?
Siehst du auch fern?

Wir malen
turnen
schwimmen
spielen
lesen
heißen Dirk und Anna.
schlafen lange.
fahren Rad.
sehen fern.

Sie
Malen Sie auch?
Turnen Sie auch?
Schwimmen Sie auch?
Spielen Sie auch?
Lesen Sie auch?
Heißen Sie Müller?
Schlafen Sie auch lange?
Fahren Sie auch Rad?
Sehen Sie auch fern?

Er/sie
Malt er auch?
Turnt sie auch?
Schwimmt er auch?
Spielt sie auch?
Liest er auch?
Heißt er Hans?
Schläft sie lange?
Fährt sie Rad?
Sieht sie fern?

2 gern — lieber — am liebsten

- Schwimmst du **gern**?
o Ja.

- Was machst du **lieber**: schwimmen oder radfahren?
o Ich fahre lieber Rad.

- Was machst du **am liebsten**?
o Ich sehe am liebsten fern.

Was machst du **lieber**:

fern**sehen** oder ... ?	Ich seh**e**		fern.
rad**fahren** oder ... ?	fahr**e**		Rad.
Klavier **spielen** oder ... ?	spiel**e**	**lieber**	Klavier.
lange **schlafen** oder ... ?	schlaf**e**		lange.
Briefe **schreiben** oder ... ?	schreib**e**		Briefe.
schwimmen oder ... ?	schwimm**e**		. —
turnen oder ... ?	turn**e**		. —
Infinitiv: ...**-en**	Ich ...**-e**		

Was machst du **nicht gern**?

Ich sehe		fern.
fahre		Rad.
spiele		Klavier.
schlafe	**nicht**	lange.
schreibe	**gern**	Briefe.
schwimme		.
turne		.

3

Klaus	ist	**hier.**	
Susi	ist	**jetzt**	bei Petra.
Wir	schwimmen	**heute.** **morgen.** **am Donnerstag.**	
Ich	spiele	**am liebsten**	Fußball.

Hier	ist	Klaus.	
Dann	gehe	ich	auch zu Petra.
Heute **Morgen** **Am Donnerstag**	schwimmen	wir	auch.
Am liebsten	spiele	ich	Fußball.

A

Wie spät ist es? 

1a
Wie heißt das auf deutsch, Tanja?
Uhr.

Richtig. Und das?
Das ist auch eine Uhr.

Gut, Tanja. Das ist ein Wecker.

1b
Sag mal, wie spät ist es?
Es ist —, es ist —, es ist eins.

Gut, Tanja. Und jetzt?
Zwei.

Das ist falsch, Tanja. Überleg mal!
Es ist drei.

Prima! Es klingelt. Die Schule ist aus. Ich gehe nach Haus.
Richtig. Und wie spät ist es jetzt?
Vier.

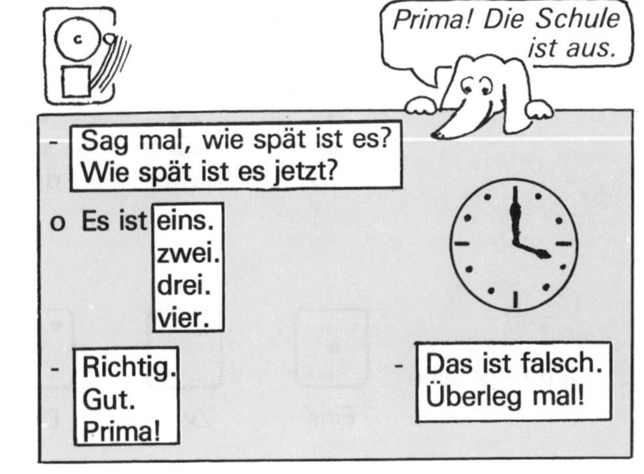

Prima! Die Schule ist aus.
- Sag mal, wie spät ist es? Wie spät ist es jetzt?
o Es ist eins. zwei. drei. vier.
- Richtig. Gut. Prima!
- Das ist falsch. Überleg mal!

A_{1a} → $Ü_1$

LEKTION 

B

Wir würfeln 

1a

1b

- Komm, wir würfeln.
o Prima. Wer fängt an?
- Du.

o Du hast eine Sechs.
Ich habe eine Drei.
Du hast gewonnen.

o Ich habe eine Vier.
Sie haben eine Fünf.
Sie haben gewonnen.

1	**2**	**3**	**4**	**5**	**6**
eins	zwei	drei	vier	fünf	sechs

Ich habe eine

Eins	Zwei	Drei	Vier	Fünf	Sechs

B_{1b} → $Ü_{2-4}$;AH_{1-2}

C

Wir telefonieren 

1

Neumann: 2-2-0-4.
Hier Meyer.

Wie bitte? Meyer? Haben Sie die Nummer 2-2-0-4?
Nein, tut mir leid. Ich habe die Nummer 2-**3**-0-4.

Entschuldigung.
Bitte.

Tut mir leid. Falsch verbunden!

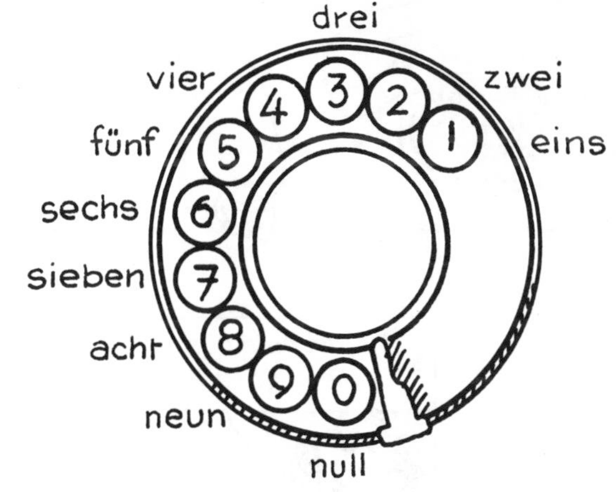
drei
zwei
eins
vier
fünf
sechs
sieben
acht
neun
null
1
2
3
4
5
6
7
8
9
0

o Hier Meyer. / Müller. / Adams.

- Haben Sie die Nummer 2-2-0-4?
o Nein, tut mir leid. Ich habe die Nummer ... .
- Entschuldigung.
o Bitte.

o Hier Tanja. / Sabine Bott.

- Hallo, Tanja. / Sabine.

Hier ist Peter (Fricke). / (Herr) Adams. / (Frau) Adams.

o Hier Müller.

- Guten Tag, Herr Müller. / Frau Müller.

$C_1 \rightarrow Ü_5$;AH_3

2 ⊕⊕

- Wie ist **deine** Telefonnummer, **Tanja**?
  Wie ist **Ihre** Telefonnummer, **Frau** Adams?

o 7-6-8-3.
  6-0-8-9.

- Danke.

D

Wie spät ist es?

⊕⊕

- Entschuldigung, wie spät ist es?

o Es ist ... . o Tut mir leid. Ich weiß es nicht.

- Danke.

$C_2 \rightarrow Ü_6; AH_7;\ D \rightarrow Ü_{7,8,10,11}; AH_{5-6}; KS_7$

Wie ist die Nummer?

Ebenso mit: ***Bauer**, Günter; ***Bauermann**, Anna usw.

F

Komm, wir telefonieren!

(02129) Haan (Vorwahl)

B

*	**Bau**, Willi Dürerstr. 70	4-6-2-9
	Baudewin, Siegfrid Friedrichstr 26	7-3-3-3
	Baudisch, Ernst Alleestr 37a	4-5-6-0
	Bauer, Folker u. Gunter Hahscheid 36	1-2-7-9
*	**Bauer**, Günter Tückmantel 33	5-1-1-6-7
*	**Bauermann**, Anna Finkenweg 12	5-1-6-9-5
*	**Bauermann**, Karl Bachstr 33	5-0-1-6-7
	Bauermann, Paula Hochdahler Str 27	7-2-9-7
*	**Baum**, Günter Kampstr 177	2-2-3-2
	Baumann, Hartmut Dürerstr 55	7-6-1-7
*	**Baumann**, Ursula Dürerstr. 63	2-6-3-0
*	**Baumbach**, Wilhelm Luisenstr. 14	3-4-1-2
	Baumgart, Horst Ohligser Str. 24	3-7-3-9
*	**Baumgarten**, Edwin Prof.Dr. Nordstr. 8	2-8-8-0
	Baurmann, Monika Neuer Markt 44	1-9-8-2
	Bauroth, Brigitte Bachstr. 162	4-6-2-7

W

	Wagner, Klaus-Günter Elberfelder Str 56	6-1-8-3
	Wagner, Luise Zeppelinstr. 8	5-1-9-0-0
*	**Wagner**, Peter Jägerstr 9	5-0-7-0-9
	Wagner, Robert Kampstr. 11	7-6-2-1
	Wahle, Heinz Textilling. Königsberger Str 12	1-7-3-3
	Wahlefeld, Helene Flemingstr. 29	5-0-1-4-2
*	**Wahlen**, Friedhelm Maler Ellscheider Str 8	5-0-2-0-6
	Wahler, K. Martin-Luther Str 2	4-5-9-1
*	**Wahler**, Wolfgang Wiedenhofer Str 40	2-9-6-0
*	**Wald**, Elke Blücherstr. 8	6-2-8-0
	Waldhauer, Günter Goerdelerstr. 10	1-0-7-8
	Waldschmidt, Alfred Alsenstr. 33	6-1-2-9

(Aus dem Telefonbuch der Stadt Haan).

G 

Wer ist dort?

Klingelingeling, wer kennt den Ton?
Ach, das ist das Telefon.
"Hier ist Peter, wer ist dort?
Mein Papa ist leider fort;
doch heut' mittag um halb vier
ist mein Vati wieder hier.
Bitteschön, Herr Klingelmann,
rufen Sie doch wieder an!"

Werner Halle

E → $AH_{4,7}$

LEKTION 

Mach bitte das Buch auf!

Mach bitte das Buch auf:
Seite 10!

Mach bitte das Buch zu!

Mach bitte das Heft auf!

Lies bitte!

Komm bitte!/Komm mal her!

Komm bitte an die Tafel!

Schreib bitte ... an die Tafel!

Setz dich bitte!

Sprich nicht!

Noch einmal bitte.

Falsch./Richtig.

Macht bitte das Buch auf:
Seite 10!

Macht bitte das Buch zu!

Macht bitte das Heft auf!

Lest bitte!

Kommt bitte!

Kommt bitte an die Tafel!

Schreibt bitte ... an die Tafel!

Setzt euch bitte!

Sprecht nicht!

Wir lesen

HEIKO
sprich nicht!

Wo warst du gestern?
Heiko spricht gern.

Guten Tag, Kinder!
Das ist Ulrich.
Ulrich, komm,
setz dich! Hier.
Das ist Herr Talmann.

Macht bitte das Hausheft auf!
Nein! Ich lese lieber.

Hallo, Ulrich. Ich bin Heiko.
Liest du auch gern Asterix?
Was machst du denn da?
Komm mal her!

Was ist denn das?
Asterix.
Setz dich und mach das Heft zu!

Heiko macht das Asterix-Heft zu.

Spielst du gern Fußball?
Ja.
Ich auch.
Heiko, sprich nicht! Komm bitte an die Tafel!

Hier ist Kreide. Schreib „Tanja ist eine Puppe" an die Tafel!
Wie bitte?

Falsch, Heiko. Setz dich!
Tanja ist eine Pupe

Pst, Ulrich! Was machst du lieber? Lesen oder radfahren?
Ich lese lieber.
Ich nicht.
Sprich nicht, Heiko! Mach dein Buch auf und lies!

Wo ist denn dein Buch?
... äh ... äh ... zu Hause.

Wie? Zu Hause?

Macht das Buch auf: Seite 10! Lest bitte!

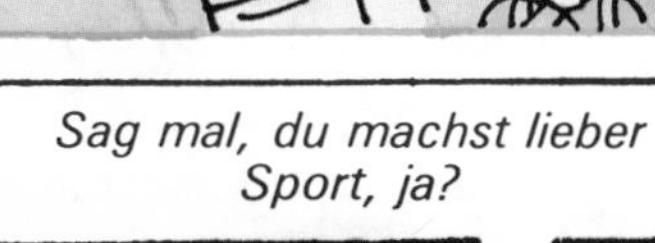

Sag mal, du machst lieber Sport, ja?

Nein, ich mache am liebsten Deutsch. Und Herr Talmann ist prima.

Na so was! Du sprichst ja schon wieder, Heiko.
Entschuldigung, Herr Talmann.

H → Wir lesen → $Ü_9$; AH_{8-9}; KS_8

1 Dialoge

Beispiel:
- Wie heißt das auf deutsch?
o Uhr.
- Richtig. Das ist eine Uhr.

- ... ... ?
o Füller.
- ....

- ... ... ?
o Puppe.
- ....

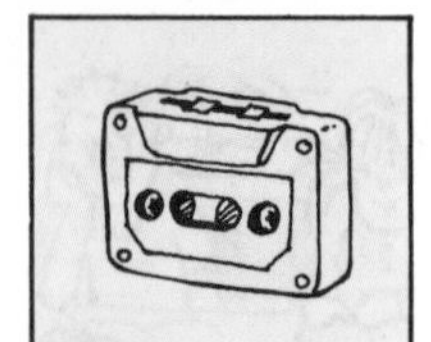

- ... ... ?
o Kassette.
- ....

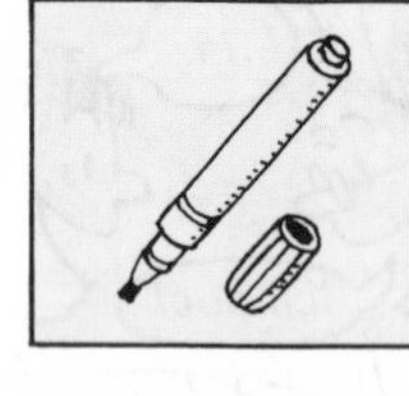

Beispiel:
- Wie heißt das auf deutsch?
o Spitzer.
- Falsch. Überleg mal!
o Ach ja, natürlich.
Das ist ein Filzstift.

- ... ... ?
o Buch.
- ....

- ... ... ?
o Landkarte.
- ....

- ... ... ?
o Wand.
- ....

2 **Wie heißen die Glückszahlen** von Fritz, Willi und Ina?
Diese Zahlen kommen auf den Bildern am häufigsten vor.

Fritz: Meine Glückszahl ist die ... .

Willi: Meine Glückszahl ist die Fünf.

Ina: Meine Glückszahl ist die ... .

3 Du würfelst mit Peter

Wer hat gewonnen? Was sagst du?

Ich habe eine ... .
Du hast eine ... .
Ich habe gewonnen.
Du hast gewonnen.

      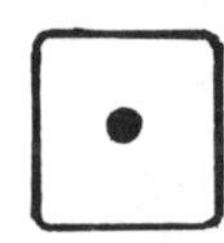  

Du

   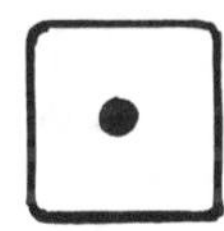     

4 Du würfelst mit Herrn Talmann

Wer hat gewonnen? Was sagst du?

Ich habe eine ... .
Sie haben eine ... .
Ich habe gewonnen.
Sie haben gewonnen.

  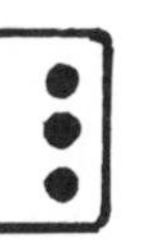   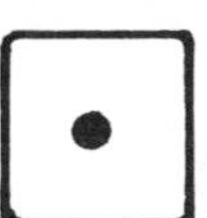    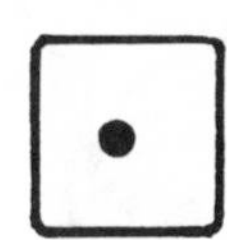

Du

        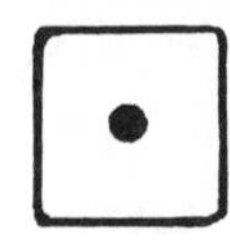

5 Dialoge

Beispiele:

- Neumann: 6-6-9-3.
- o Hier Adams.
- Adams? Haben Sie die Nummer 6-6-9-3?
- o Tut mir leid. Ich habe die Nummer 6-6-**8**-3.
- Entschuldigung.
- o Bitte.

- Müller: 8-4-9-8.
- o Hier Müller.
- Guten Tag, Herr Müller. Hier ist ... . Ist Petra zu Hause?
- o Ja, ... Petra, komm! Hier ist ... .

6 Dialoge. Beispiele:

- Wie ist deine Telefonnummer?
- o Meine Nummer ist 7-3-5-9.
- Danke.

- Wie ist Ihre Telefonnummer?
- o Meine Nummer ist 6-0-2-8.
- Danke.

7 Dialoge

Beispiele:

- Entschuldigung, wie spät ist es?
o Es ist sechs.
- Danke.

- Entschuldigung, wie spät ist es?
o Tut mir leid. Ich weiß es nicht.

8 Wie spät ist es?

Die meisten Uhren gehen richtig.
Wie spät ist es?

Es ist ... .

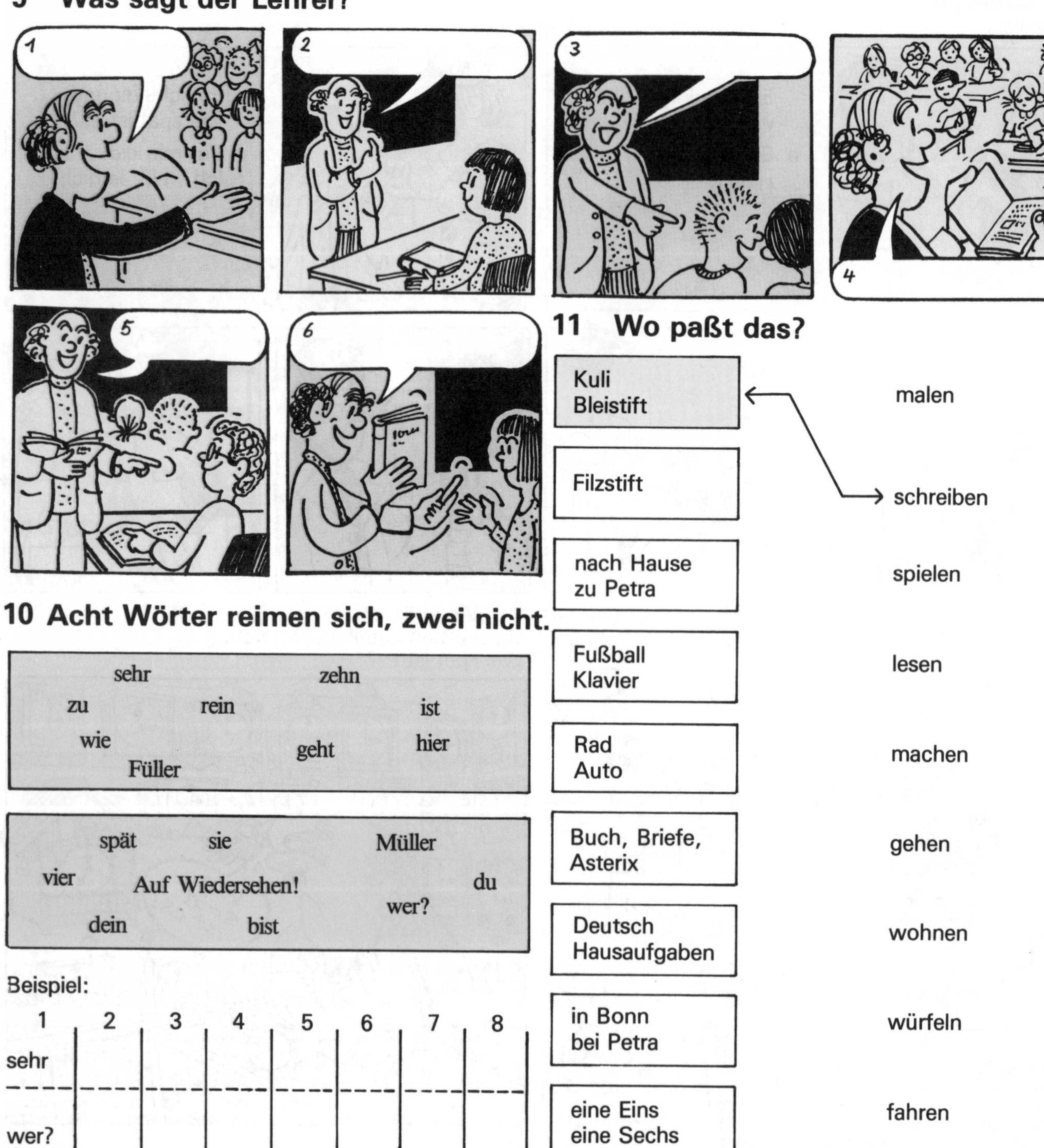

9 Was sagt der Lehrer?

1

2

3

4

5

6

10 Acht Wörter reimen sich, zwei nicht.

sehr zehn zu rein ist wie geht hier Füller

spät sie Müller vier Auf Wiedersehen! du wer? dein bist

Beispiel:

1	2	3	4	5	6	7	8
sehr							
wer?							

11 Wo paßt das?

Kuli Bleistift	malen
Filzstift	schreiben
nach Hause zu Petra	spielen
Fußball Klavier	lesen
Rad Auto	machen
Buch, Briefe, Asterix	gehen
Deutsch Hausaufgaben	wohnen
in Bonn bei Petra	würfeln
eine Eins eine Sechs	fahren

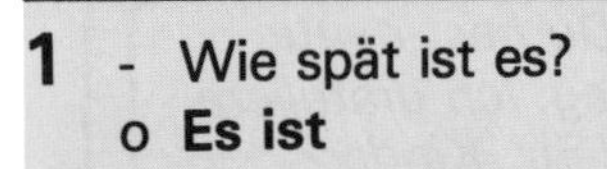

1 - Wie spät ist es?
o **Es ist**

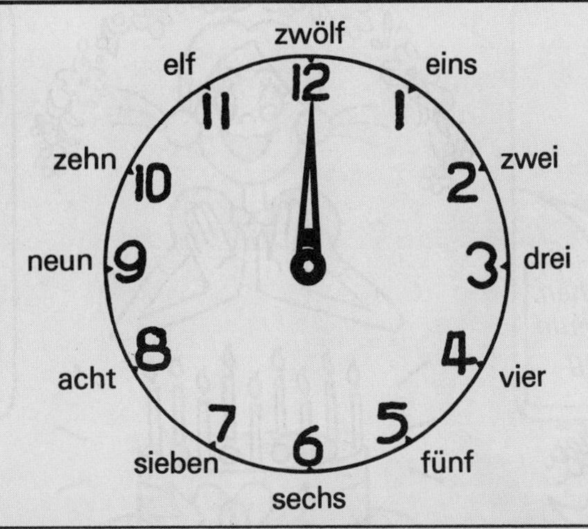

2 - Komm, wir | würfeln. / schwimmen. / fahren Rad.

o Prima!

3 **Ich habe** usw.

Ich habe | eine Drei.

Wir haben | eine Fünf.

Hast du | eine Eins?

Haben Sie | eine Sechs?

Hat er/sie | eine Zwei?

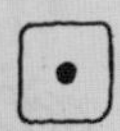

4 Wie ist | deine / Ihre | Telefonnummer, Hans? / , Frau Adams?

5 **Das hörst du in der Schule.**

Mach	-	das Buch auf!	Mach	t	das Buch auf!
Mach	-	das Buch zu!	Mach	t	das Buch zu!
Schreib	-	... an die Tafel!	Schreib	t	... an die Tafel!
Überleg	-	mal!	Überleg	t	mal!
Lies	-	!	Les	t	!
Sprich	-	nicht!	Sprech	t	nicht!

LEKTION 7

Ich habe heute Geburtstag

1

Was ist denn das? Ein Kuchen?
Ja, ein Kuchen. Ich habe heute Geburtstag.

So. Du hast heute Geburtstag. Ich gratuliere. Und ihr, Kinder?
Wir gratulieren auch.

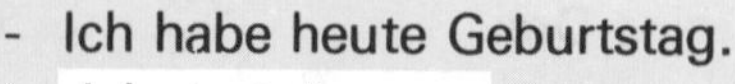

- Ich habe heute Geburtstag.

o Ich gratuliere.
Wir gratulieren.

2

Wie alt bist du, Tanja?
Raten Sie mal!

Ein Kuchen mit neun Kerzen. Ich bin ...

Ach ja, natürlich. Du bist neun Jahre alt.

- Wie alt bist du?

o Ich bin ... Jahre alt.

o Rat mal!

o Raten Sie mal!

Er ist ein Jahr alt.

$A_2 \rightarrow AH_{1-5}$

3

- Na so was! Wir haben **kein Geschenk/keine Geschenke.**
o Doch, doch. Wir haben **Geschenke.**

B Der .../das .../die ... ist aber schön

B → $Ü_1$;AH_6;KS_9

Geschenke

ein — der	ein — das	eine — die

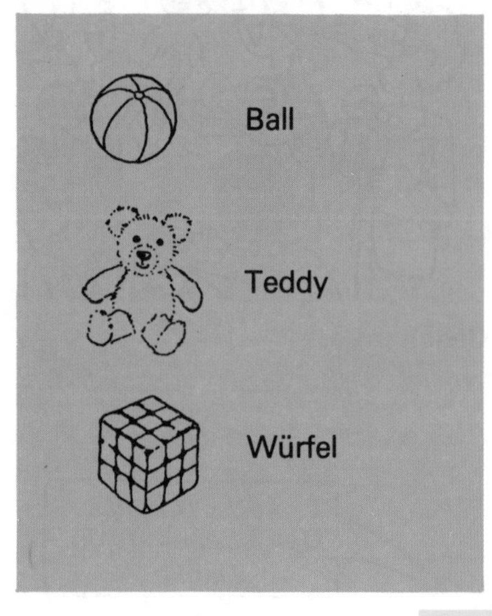

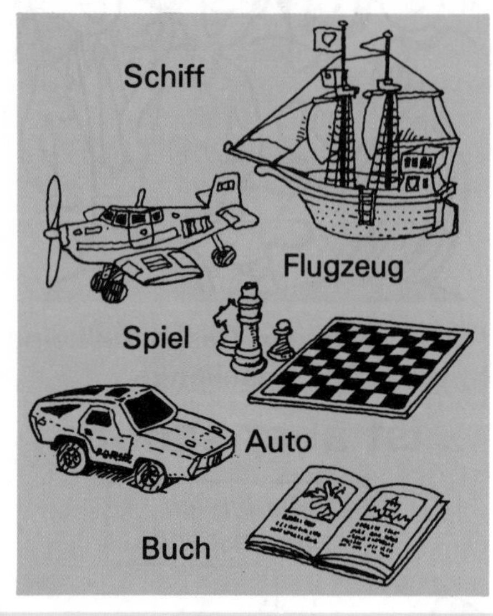

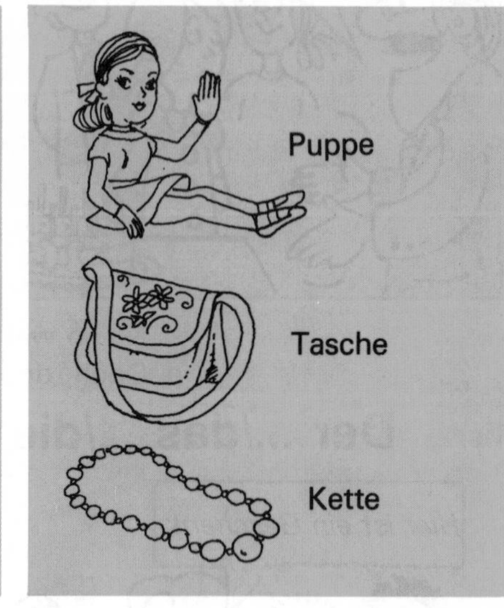

- Ich gratuliere, Tanja. Hier ist ein Geschenk.
o Danke. Da bin ich aber gespannt.

o Oh, ein Ball!
Der ist aber schön.

o Oh, ein Spiel!
Das ist aber schön.

o Oh, eine Puppe!
Die ist aber schön.

C Tanja hat im ... Geburtstag

Tanja hat im ... Wer hat auch im ...

Januar	April	Juli	Oktober
Februar	Mai	August	November
März	Juni	September	Dezember

... Geburtstag. ... Geburtstag?

Und wann hast du Geburtstag?

C → $Ü_2$;AH_7

D

1 Und wer im ... Geburtstag hat, tritt ein

Das war aber schön.
Und wer im Januar Geburts tag hat, tritt ein, tritt ein, tritt ein.
Tanja, dreh dich, Tanja, dreh dich im Kreise he — rum, — rum.

2. Und wer im Februar Geburtstag hat, tritt ein, tritt ein,
tritt ein. ..., dreh dich, ...
usw.

2 Wer hat im ... Geburtstag?

Wie viele Kinder hier haben im ... Geburtstag?

... Kinder haben im Januar ...	... Kinder haben im April ...	... Kinder haben im Juli ...	... Kinder haben im Oktober	... Geburtstag.
... Kinder haben im Februar ...	... Kinder haben im Mai ...	... Kinder haben im August ...	... Kinder haben im November	... Geburtstag.
... Kinder haben im März ...	... Kinder haben im Juni ...	... Kinder haben im September ..	... Kinder haben im Dezember	... Geburtstag.

- **Wie viele** Kinder hier haben im Mai Geburtstag?
o Drei.

$D_2 \rightarrow Ü_3; AH_{8-9}$

LEKTION 7

Wir lesen 

Ich gratuliere.
Hier ist ein Geschenk.

Vielen Dank.
Was ist es denn?
Rat mal!

Eine Platte! Oh, schön.
Das ist doch deine Lieblingsgruppe.

Ich gratuliere, Susi.
Guten Tag, Monika.

Hier ist ein Geschenk.
Die Ruckizuckis! Danke.

Ist das nicht deine Lieblingsgruppe?
Doch, doch!

Wir gratulieren, Susi.
Hier ist ein Geschenk.

Oh, danke. Ist das eine Platte?

Ja, richtig. Das ist deine Lieblingsgruppe, ja?

Hier ist ein Geschenk, Susi.
Die Ruckizuckis
Die Platte ist sehr schön, Mutti, aber ....

Die Ruckizuckis

Sonderangebot!
Die Ruckizuckis nur DM 12.-
DM 22
DM 12

ÜBUNGEN 7

1 Dialoge

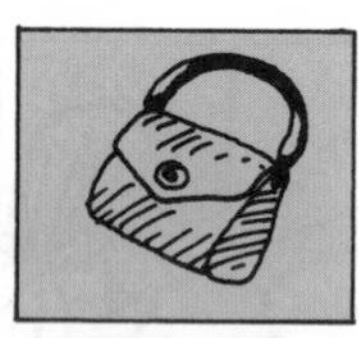

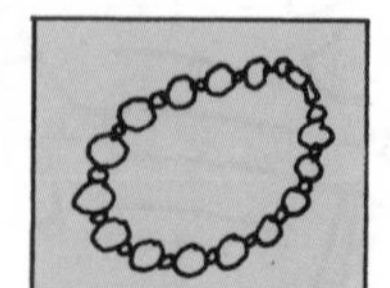

- Ich gratuliere.
  Hier ist ein Geschenk.

o Da bin ich aber gespannt.
  Oh, ein/eine ... !
  Der ... ist aber schön.
  Das ....
  Die ....
  Danke.

2 Wann habe ich Geburtstag?

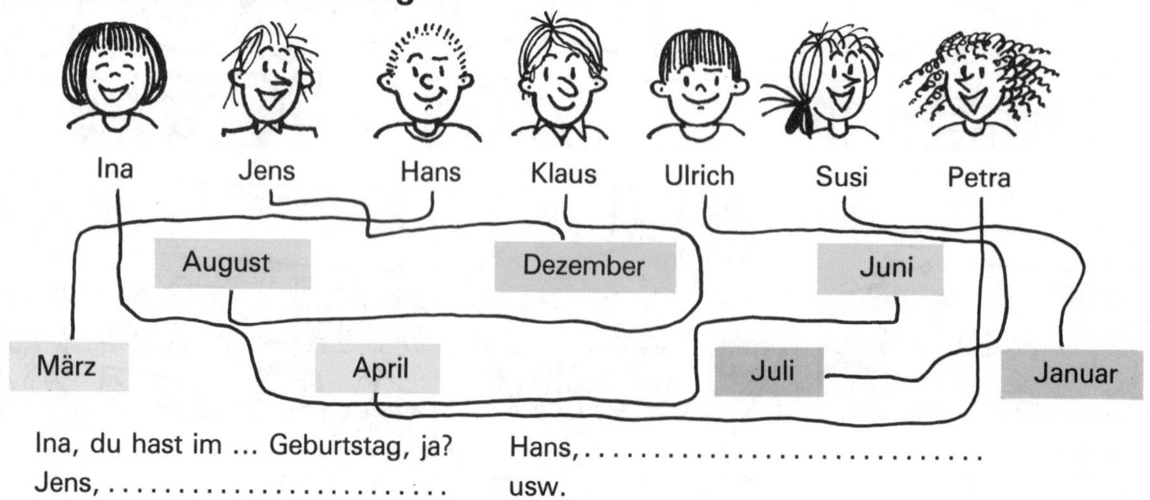

Ina, du hast im ... Geburtstag, ja?
Jens, ...
Hans, ...
usw.

3

Nina und Norbert Neugierig

a)

1. Wie heißt du?
2. Wie alt bist du?
3. Wann hast du Geburtstag?
4. Wann hat dein Freund / deine Freundin Geburtstag?
5. Wie alt ist er? / sie?
6. Wie viele Kinder hier haben im Februar Geburtstag?
7. Wie alt ist dein Bruder? / deine Schwester?
8. Wann hat er / sie Geburtstag?
9. Und dein Vater? / deine Mutter?

b)

1. Ist das deine Katze?
2. Schläft sie?
3. Wie heißt deine Katze?
4. Wie alt ist sie?
5. Wann hat sie Geburtstag?
6. Was macht deine Katze am liebsten?
7. Was macht sie nicht gern?
8. Sag mal, wie spät ist es?
9. Gehst du jetzt rein?

7

GRAMMATIK
KNACKER
Knacker knackt jede Nuß!

1

ich wir	er/sie	du Sie ihr

2

Ich habe | heute Geburtstag. Wir haben | heute Geburtstag.		Hast du auch heute Geburtstag? Haben Sie auch heute Geburtstag?
	Er/sie hat | heute nicht Geburtstag. Die Kinder haben | morgen Geburtstag.	

3

- Wie alt ist dein Bruder/deine Schwester?
o Mein Bruder/meine Schwester ist
ein Jahr alt **zwei Jahre alt** **drei Jahre alt** **vier Jahre alt**

4

der — ein	das — ein	die — eine
Ball	Spiel	Puppe
Teddy	Auto	Tasche
Würfel	Buch	Kette
Füller	Schiff	Tür
Bleistift	Flugzeug	Tafel
Block	Telefon	Landkarte
Stuhl	Fenster	Wand
Kuli	Heft	Kassette
Radiergummi	Bild	Tasche
Spitzer	Lineal	Lampe
Filzstift	Geschenk	Schreibmaschine
Tisch		Kerze
Kuchen		

- Ich gratuliere. Hier ist ein Geschenk.
o Da bin ich aber gespannt!

- **ein** Ball. o Oh, **der** ist aber schön!	- **ein** Spiel. o Oh, **das** ist aber schön!	- **eine** Puppe. o Oh, **die** ist aber schön!

5 Fragen und Antworten

ANTWORTEN	W – FRAGEN	
Das ist Peter.	**Wer**	ist (denn) das?
Ich heiße Jens.	**Wie**	heißt du?
Haus.	**Wie**	heißt das auf deutsch?
8-4-9-8.	**Wie**	ist deine Telefonnummer?
Ich bin neun Jahre alt.	**Wie alt**	bist du?
Es ist drei.	**Wie spät**	ist es?
Drei.	**Wie viele**	Kinder hier haben im Mai Geburtstag?
Ich schreibe Briefe.	**Was**	machst du?
Das ist ein Geschenk.	**Was**	ist denn das?
Ich wohne in Bonn.	**Wo**	wohnst du?
Am Sonntag.	**Wann**	schläfst du lange?
Heute ist Dienstag.	**Welcher Tag**	ist heute?

A

Wo habe ich bloß ...? 

1

Ebenso mit:

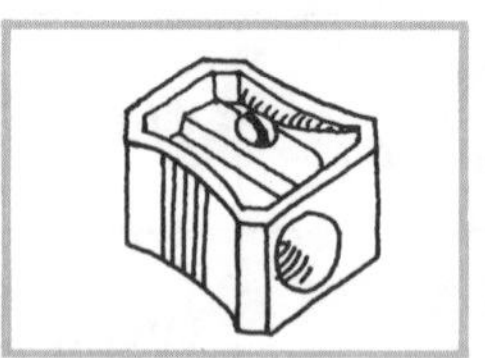

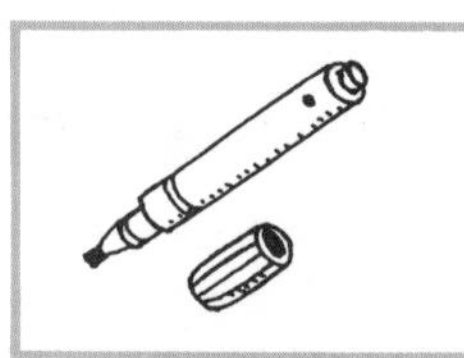

- Wo habe ich bloß meinen Kuli?
  Kann ich mal deinen (Kuli) haben?
o Hier.
- Danke.

$A_1 \rightarrow Ü_1$

2

3

- Wo habe ich bloß meinen Füller?
  Mein Füller schreibt nicht.
  Mein Füller ist leer.

o Nimm meinen (Füller)!
  Nehmen Sie meinen (Füller)!

- Danke.

4

Ebenso mit:

   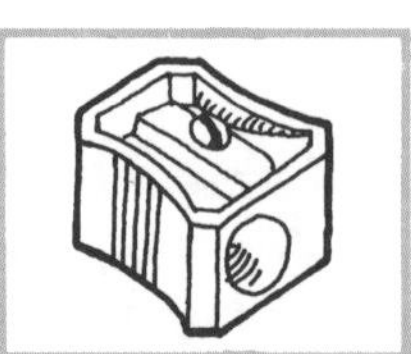 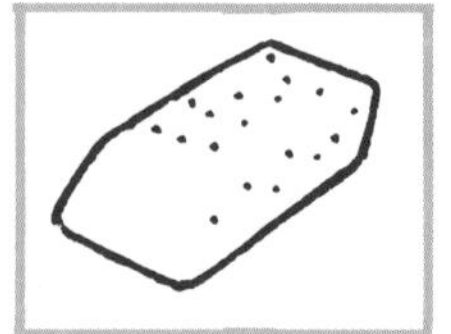 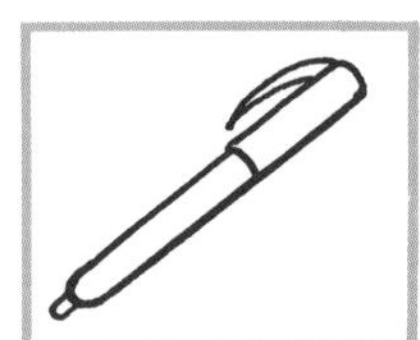

- Kann ich mal deinen Bleistift haben?

o Hier. - Danke.	o Tut mir leid. Ich habe keinen Bleistift.

$A_4 \rightarrow AH_{1-4}$

Tombola und Würfelspiel

1

Ebenso mit:

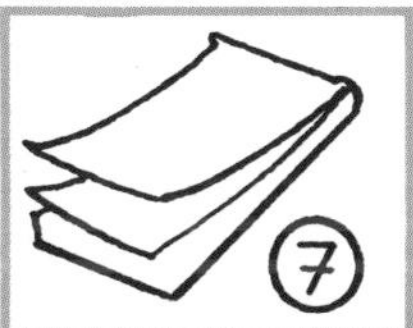

2

Ebenso mit:

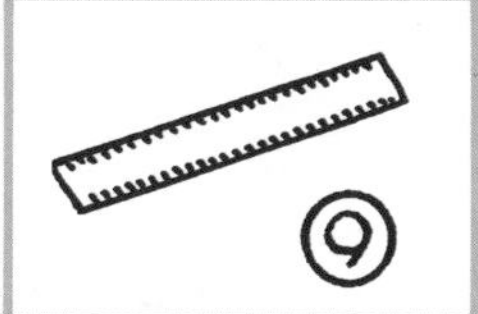

Und was bekomme ich?

Einen Knochen!

LEKTION 

3

Tanja:
Kommen Sie, wir würfeln.

Lehrer:
Gern.

Lehrer:
Komm, Tanja, wir würfeln.

Tanja:
Gern.

Lehrer:
Was hast du?

Tanja:
Eine Drei.

Tanja:
Was haben Sie?

Lehrer:
Eine Vier.

Tanja:
Und Sie, was haben Sie?

Lehrer:
Eine Fünf.

Lehrer:
Und was hast du?

Tanja:
Eine Sechs.

Tanja:
Sie haben gewonnen.
Sie bekommen eine Uhr.

Lehrer:
Du hast gewonnen, Tanja.
Du bekommst eine Kette.

Ebenso mit:

- Wer hat die Nummer ...?
o Ich.
- Du hast gewonnen.
  Sie haben gewonnen.
  Gratuliere. Du bekommst
  Gratuliere. Sie bekommen einen Spitzer | ein Buch | eine Uhr.

- Kommen Sie, Herr Müller, wir würfeln.
  Komm, Tanja, wir würfeln.
o Gern.

- Was hast du, Tanja?
  Was haben Sie, Herr Müller?
o Eine ... .
- Du hast gewonnen, Tanja.
  Sie haben gewonnen, Herr Müller.

$B_3 \rightarrow Ü_{2-4}$

Brüder und Schwestern

1

Hast du eine Schwester?
Nein, ich habe keine Schwester,

... aber ich habe einen Bruder.

Wie heißt er?
Ulrich!

Ich habe	keinen Bruder, keine Schwester,	aber ich habe	eine Schwester. einen Bruder.

- Wie heißt er?
o Ulrich.

- Wie heißt sie?
o Sabine.

Ich habe nur eine Schwester.

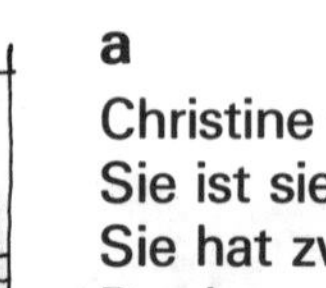

2

a

Christine wohnt in Frankfurt.
Sie ist sieben Jahre alt.
Sie hat zwei Schwestern, aber keinen Bruder.
Christine hat einen Hund.
Er heißt Hasso
und spielt gern mit Christine.
Hasso hat ein Hobby:
er sieht gern fern.

b

Ina, fünf Jahre alt, wohnt in München. Sie malt gern. Sie hat keine Schwester, aber sie hat einen Bruder. Er heißt Michael und ist sieben Jahre alt. Ina hat eine Katze: Muschi. Muschi schläft und spielt gern. Sie ist ein Jahr alt.

c

Das ist Jens. Jens wohnt in Hamburg. Er hat zwei Brüder: Lutz und Christian. Jens ist acht Jahre alt, Lutz ist zehn, und Christian ist zwölf. Jens spielt gern Fußball und fährt gern Rad, Lutz schwimmt gern, und Christian spielt am liebsten Klavier.

Ich habe	einen Bruder. eine Schwester.	zwei Brüder. zwei Schwestern. Geschwister.

$C_2 \rightarrow Ü_5$;AH_6

LEKTION 8

Was ist richtig?

		RICHTIG	FALSCH
a			
1	Christine hat zwei Brüder und eine Schwester.	☐	☐
2	Christine hat eine Katze.	☐	☐
3	Hasso spielt gern mit Christine und sieht gern fern.	☐	☐
b			
4	Ina ist fünf Jahre alt.	☐	☐
5	Sie malt gern.	☐	☐
6	Sie hat eine Schwester, aber sie hat keinen Bruder.	☐	☐
7	Muschi ist eine Katze.	☐	☐
8	Muschi ist zwei Jahre alt.	☐	☐
9	Muschi spielt nicht gern.	☐	☐
c			
10	Jens wohnt in Hamburg.	☐	☐
11	Jens hat zwei Brüder: Lutz und Ulrich.	☐	☐
12	Jens spielt gern Klavier und fährt gern Rad.	☐	☐
13	Lutz schwimmt gern.	☐	☐

3 Und du?

Hast du

einen Bruder?	zwei oder drei Brüder?	keinen Bruder?
eine Schwester?	zwei oder drei Schwestern?	keine Schwester?
einen Hund?		
eine Katze?		

Wie

heißt	dein Bruder/deine Schwester/dein Hund/deine Katze?
heißen	deine Geschwister/deine Hunde/deine Katzen?
alt ist	dein Bruder/deine Schwester/dein Hund/deine Katze?
alt sind	deine Geschwister/deine Hunde/deine Katzen?

Was braucht ...?

1a

Frau Talmann braucht einen ... .

Peter braucht einen ... .

Ina braucht einen ... .

1b

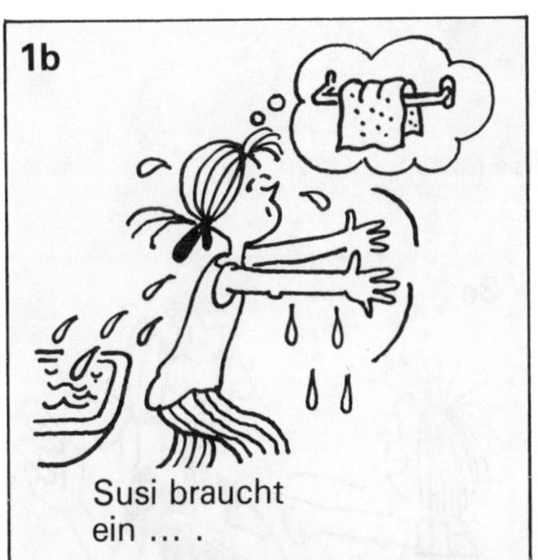

Susi braucht ein ... .

Regen-schirm	Kamm	Pinsel
Handtuch		Pflaster
Brief-marke	Schere	Schnur

Peter braucht ein ... .

1c

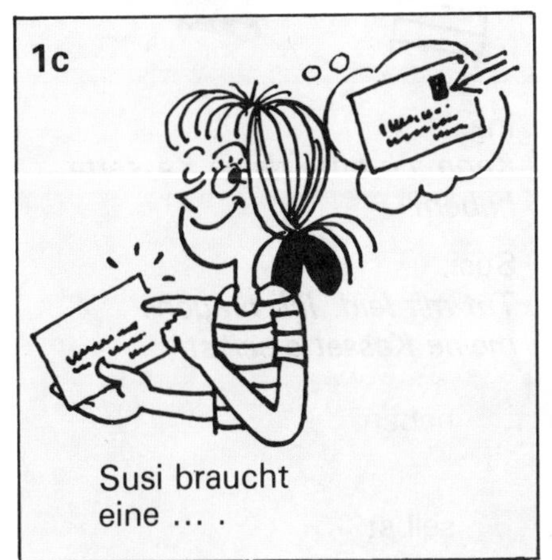

Susi braucht eine ... .

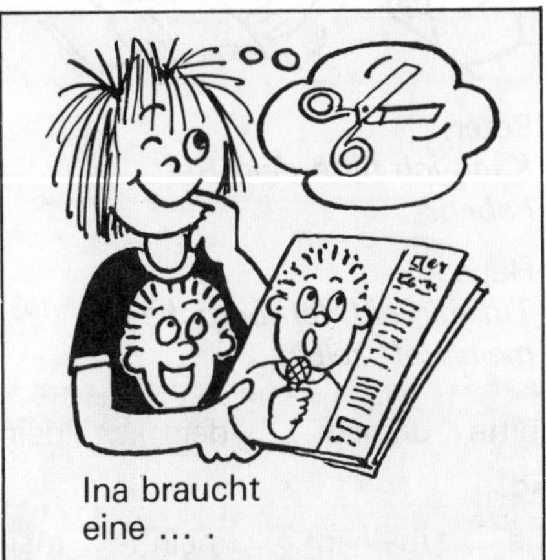

Ina braucht eine ... .

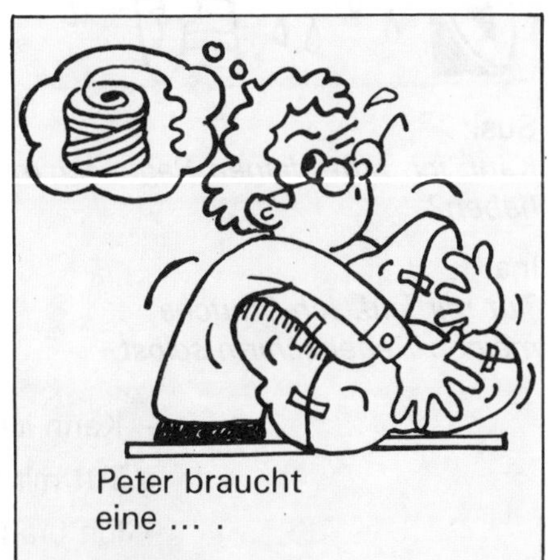

Peter braucht eine ... .

Ich brauche einen Hundekuchen.

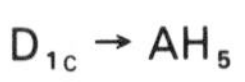

$D_{1c} \rightarrow AH_5$

LEKTION 

2a

Peter:
Ich brauche einen Spitzer.

Susi:
Tut mir leid. Ich habe keinen Spitzer.

2b

Herr Talmann:
Ich brauche ein Streichholz.

Herr Müller:
Tut mir leid. Ich habe kein Streichholz.

2c

Ina:
Ich brauche eine Schere.

Peter:
Tut mir leid. Ich habe keine Schere.

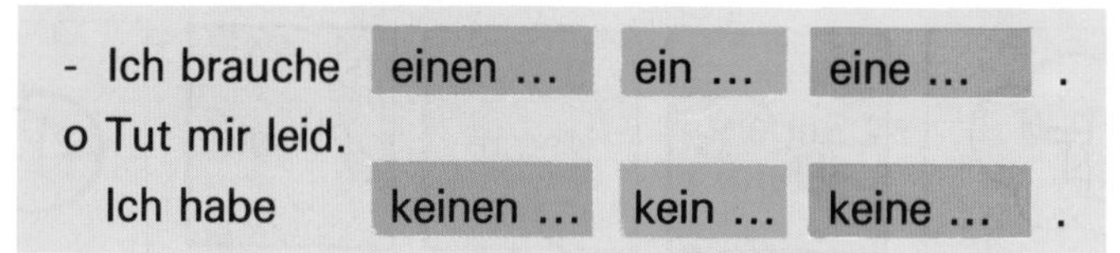

- Ich brauche	einen ...	ein ...	eine ...	.
o Tut mir leid.				
Ich habe	keinen ...	kein ...	keine ...	.

3a

Susi:
Kann ich bitte deinen Regenschirm haben?

Ina:
Tut mir leid. Ich brauche meinen Regenschirm selbst.

3b

Peter:
Kann ich bitte dein Heft haben?

Hans:
Tut mir leid. Ich brauche mein Heft selbst.

3c

Ina:
Kann ich bitte deine Kassette haben?

Susi:
Tut mir leid. Ich brauche meine Kassette selbst.

- Kann ich bitte	deinen ...	dein ...	deine ...	haben?
o Tut mir leid.				
Ich brauche	meinen ...	mein ...	meine ...	selbst.

D_{3a} → $Ü_{6-7}$;AH_7;KS_{10}

1 Wir fragen

Beispiel:

Wo habe ich bloß meinen Kuli? Kann ich mal deinen (Kuli) haben?

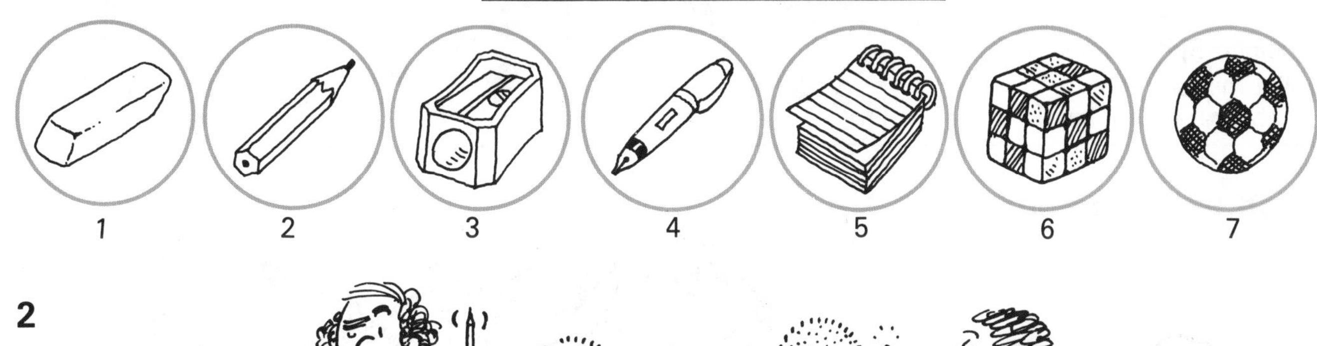

2

- Wo habe ich bloß meinen Bleistift? o Nehmen Sie meinen (Bleistift)!

- Wo habe ich bloß meinen Spitzer? o Nimm meinen (Spitzer)!

3 Dialoge

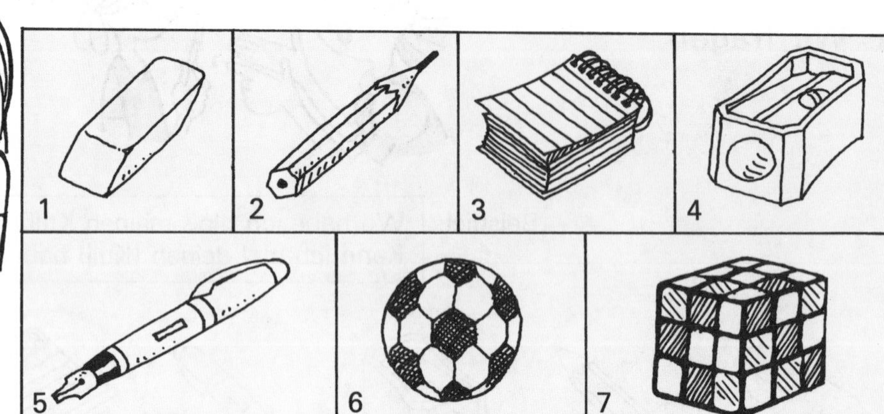

Beispiel:

- Kann ich mal deinen Spitzer haben?
o Tut mir leid. Ich habe keinen (Spitzer).

4 Ich habe gewonnen!

Beispiel:

Susi: Ich habe gewonnen! Was bekomme ich?
Mann: Du bekommst ein Spiel.
Susi: Danke.

5 Du bist Thilo ... . Was sagst du?

Thilo: *Ich habe einen Bruder und ....*
Birgit: *Ich habe ....* Markus: .... Manuela: .... usw.

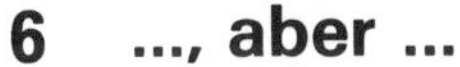

6 ..., aber ...

Beispiel:

Frau Talmann hat einen Regenschirm,
aber Peter hat keinen (Regenschirm).

7 Dialoge

Beispiel:

- Kann ich bitte deinen Filzstift haben?
o Tut mir leid.
  Ich brauche meinen Filzstift selbst.

- Kann ich bitte deinen Regenschirm haben?
o Hier.
- Danke.

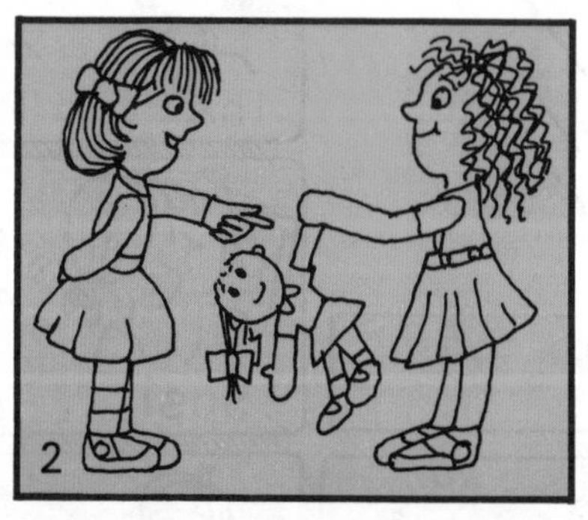

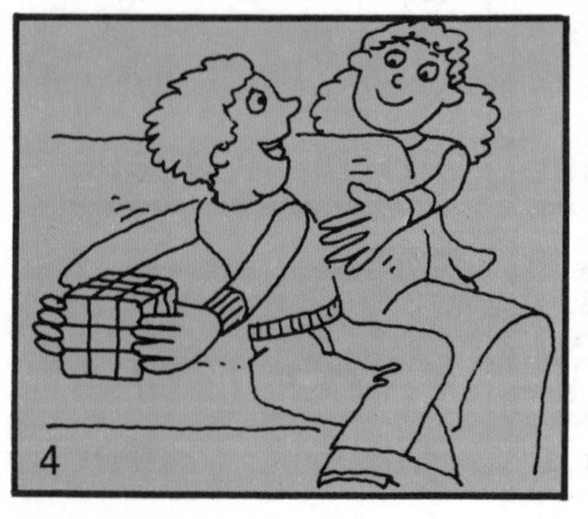

GRAMMATIK
KNACKER
Knacker knackt jede Nuß!
8

1 meinen - deinen ← der - ein - mein / Kuli Bleistift..................

- Wo habe ich bloß	meinen Kuli?	
Kann ich mal	deinen (Kuli)	haben?
o Ja, **nimm**	meinen (Kuli),	Peter!

- Wo habe ich bloß	meinen Kuli?	
Kann ich mal	deinen (Kuli)	haben?
o Ja, **nehmen Sie**	meinen (Kuli),	Herr Adams!

2 Mein Kuli | ist leer. / schreibt nicht.

3 Komm, Peter, / Kommen Sie, Herr Müller, | wir würfeln.

4

- Kann ich mal	deinen Kuli	haben?
o Ich habe	keinen Kuli.	

5 ein Bruder - zwei Br**ü**der
eine Schwester - zwei Schwester**n**

Wie	heißen	deine Brüder?
	alt sind	deine Schwestern?

6 und/aber

Ich habe einen Hund **und** (ich habe) eine Katze.
Susi hat **kein**en Hund, **aber** (sie hat) eine Katze.

7

Ich habe	einen	ein	eine	
bekomme	keinen	kein	keine	
brauche	meinen	mein	meine	
Kann ich mal	deinen	dein	deine	haben?
	Füller	Buch	Kette	
	Spitzer	Heft	Puppe	
	Ball	Lineal	Tasche	
	usw.	usw.	usw.	
	der - ein	das - ein	die - eine	

LEKTION 

Der Regenbogen 

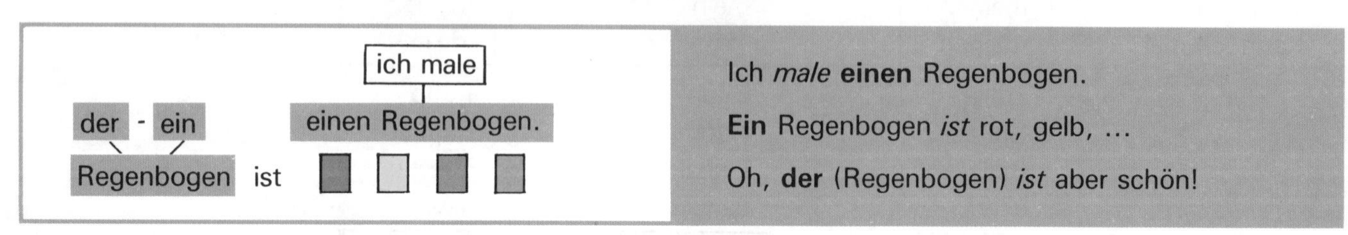

A → AH_1

B

Das Zebra 

1

- Ich möchte malen. Darf ich?

o Ja. Natürlich. Ja, natürlich.	o Nein. Natürlich nicht.

Hier ist Rot.
Hier sind Rot, Grün und Gelb.
Da hast du Blau.

2

—O—

Ja, das Zebra ist (sehr) schön.	Nein, das Zebra ist nicht schön.
Ja, das Zebra ist toll.	Nein, das Zebra ist furchtbar.

ich male
ein Zebra.
das - ein
Zebra
ist
und

Ich *male* **ein** Zebra.

Ein Zebra *ist* schwarz und weiß.

So. Das *ist* **das** Zebra.

- Blau, bitte.
o Da hast du Blau.

Ein Zebra **ist doch nicht** blau!
Ein Zebra ist weiß und schwarz.

C Die Maus und die Katze

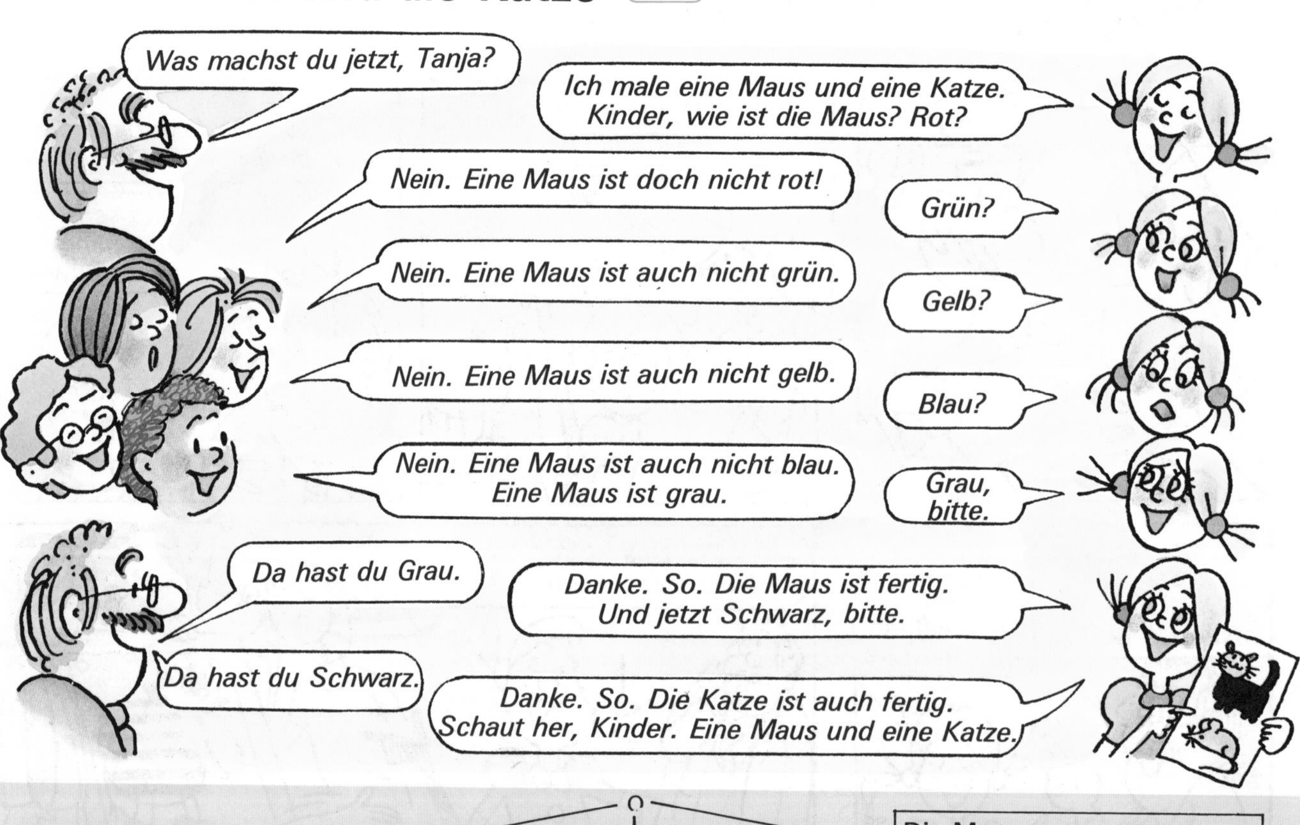

Was machst du jetzt, Tanja?
Ich male eine Maus und eine Katze. Kinder, wie ist die Maus? Rot?
Nein. Eine Maus ist doch nicht rot!
Grün?
Nein. Eine Maus ist auch nicht grün.
Gelb?
Nein. Eine Maus ist auch nicht gelb.
Blau?
Nein. Eine Maus ist auch nicht blau. Eine Maus ist grau.
Grau, bitte.
Da hast du Grau.
Danke. So. Die Maus ist fertig. Und jetzt Schwarz, bitte.
Da hast du Schwarz.
Danke. So. Die Katze ist auch fertig. Schaut her, Kinder. Eine Maus und eine Katze.

Die Maus / Die Katze ist toll/(sehr) schön.

Die Maus ist schön, aber die Katze ist furchtbar.

Die Maus / Die Katze ist aber furchtbar.

Das ist doch keine Maus! / keine Katze!

ich male
eine Maus.

die - eine
Maus ist grau.

Ich *male* **eine** Maus.

Eine Maus *ist* doch nicht blau.

Die Maus *ist* fertig.

Was machst du?

Ich male (ein Bild).

Und was malst du?

Ich male **einen Regenbogen.**
ein Zebra.
eine Maus/Katze.

Wie machst du das?
Was brauchst du dazu?

Ich nehme Rot/Gelb/Grün/........ .
Ich brauche Rot/Gelb/.............. .
Schwarz, bitte.

Da hast du Schwarz./Da.
Wie? **Ein Regenbogen**
ist doch nicht schwarz!

Grün, bitte.

Da hast du Grün./Da.
Wie? **Ein Zebra** ist doch nicht grün!

Rot, bitte.

Da hast du Rot./Da.
Wie? **Eine Maus/Katze**
ist doch nicht rot!

Schaut her, Kinder!

Der Regenbogen
Das Zebra
Die Maus/Katze
ist fertig.

Oh, der (Regenbogen)/das (Zebra)/die (Maus/Katze)
ist

toll/(sehr) schön.

Du malst aber (sehr) gut.

aber furchtbar.
Das ist doch kein .../keine ... !
Du malst aber nicht gut.

C → $Ü_{1-2}$;AH_2;KS_{11}

Der Regenbogen

Ein Regenbogen,

komm und schau:

rot und orange,

gelb, grün und blau.

Josef Guggenmoos

Verkehrsschild

Was wollen wir malen?

Du und ich?

Du malst ein Dreieck, △

ich einen Strich. |

Dein Dreieck ist rot.

Mein Strich springt hinein.

Das Zeichen ist fertig.

Was mag es wohl sein?

Hildegard Wohlgemuth

Kannst du das Verkehrsschild malen?

D → KS_{14}

E

Wir malen Tiere

einen	
	Stier
	Papagei
	Fisch
	Hund
	Frosch
	Esel
	Tiger

ein	
	Pferd
	Kamel
	Schwein
	Huhn
	Krokodil
	Schaf
	Lama

eine	
	Kuh
	Ente
	Schnecke
	Katze
	Gans
	Ziege
	Schlange

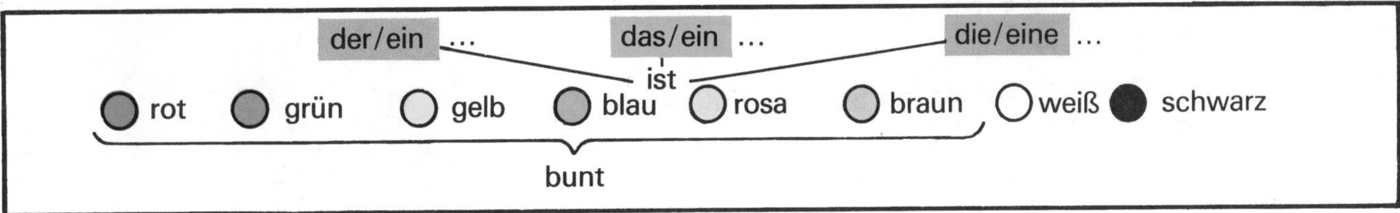

E → $Ü_{4-6}$; AH_{3-5}; KS_{12-13}

LEKTION 

F

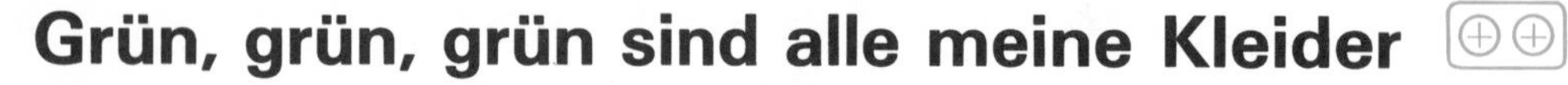

Grün, grün, grün sind alle meine Kleider

2 Blau, blau, blau ...
weil mein Schatz 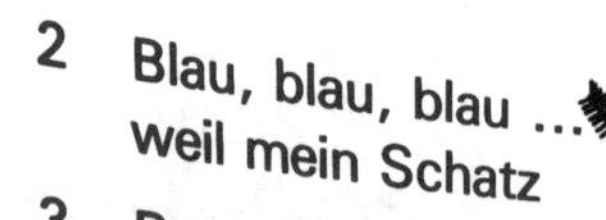 ein Seemann ist.

3 Rot, rot, rot ...
weil mein Schatz ein Feuerwehrmann ist.

4 Weiß, weiß, weiß ...
weil mein Schatz ein Bäcker, Bäcker ist.

5 Schwarz, schwarz, schwarz ...
weil mein Schatz ein Schornsteinfeger ist.

6 Bunt, bunt, bunt ...
weil mein Schatz ein Maler, Maler ist.

Wir lesen

Susi Schlaksig

ist klein ist groß ist riesengroß

LEKTION 

Susi Schlaksig

Susi ist mit Petra bei Tante Hilde, aber Tante Hilde ist nicht zu Hause. Tante Hilde hat drei Katzen: Mieze, Schnurri und Muschi. Aber wer ist Mieze? Wer Schnurri? Und wer ist Muschi? Susi, schau her! Hier ist ein Zettel.

MIEZE ist schwarz und weiß. Sie ist groß.
SCHNURRI ist klein. Sie ist schwarz und zwölf Jahre alt.
MUSCHI ist auch klein, aber sie ist nicht schwarz. Sie ist grau.

Die Katze schläft. Sie ist groß, schwarz und weiß. Rat mal, wie sie heißt!

Komm, Mieze!

Schau mal. Sie ist grau.
Das ist Muschi.
Muschi schläft auch.
Und das ist Schnurri. Komm, Schnurri!

Hier ist noch eine Katze.
Sie ist riesengroß und schwarz, grau und weiß.
Aber wie heißt sie?

Petra, schau her! Hier ist ein Zettel.

Hier ist noch eine Katze. Sie ist riesengroß. Sie ist schwarz, grau und weiß. Das ist die Katze von Müllers. Sie heißt Riese.
Riese- nein! nein! nein!
Richtig! Das ist Riese.

1 Was ist fertig? Was nicht?

2 - Wie ist der Regenbogen?
o Der Regenbogen ist rot, gelb, grün und blau.
- Wie ist die Katze?
o ....
usw.

3 Was paßt nicht?

a Esel - Kamel - Schlange - Pferd
b Frosch - Papagei - Huhn - Gans
c Krokodil - Schwein - Tiger - Schlange
d Hund - Katze - Esel - Schnecke
e Pferd - Schaf - Ziege - Kuh
f Huhn - Ente - Papagei - Gans

der	das	die
...	...	Schlange

4 Was malst du, ...? Ich male .... .

Peter: *Ich male ....*

Jutta: *Ich male ....*

Ina: *Ich male ....*

Lars: ....

Sabine: ....

5 Dialoge

Beispiel:
- Du malst einen Regenbogen. Wie machst du das?
o Ich nehme Rot, Gelb, Grün und Blau.

Ebenso mit:

Haus Kuh
Frosch Schwein
Krokodil Maus
Lama Zebra

6

Na so was!
Ein Pferd ist doch nicht ... !

9
KNACKER
GRAMMATIK
Knacker knackt jede Nuß!

1

Ich | male

	einen	Regenbogen.	
	Ein	Regenbogen | ist |	rot, gelb,... .
So.	Der	Regenbogen | ist |	fertig.

Füller
Spitzer
Ball
Papagei
Hund
usw.

	ein	Zebra.	
	Ein	Zebra | ist |	weiß und schwarz.
So.	Das	Zebra | ist |	fertig.

Heft
Ball
Lineal
Pferd
Schwein
usw.

	eine	Maus.	
	Eine	Maus | ist |	grau.
So.	Die	Maus | ist |	fertig.

Kette
Puppe
Tasche
Kuh
Katze
usw.

2 Ich möchte

mal*en*. schwimm*en*. radfahr*en*. Klavier spiel*en*. Fußball spiel*en*. les*en*.
Infinitiv

Papa, darf ich?

Sag mal, wieviel ist? 

1

Wieviel ist drei mal drei?
Das ist leicht. Neun.

Richtig. Drei mal drei ist neun.

Ich rechne gut, nicht?
Ja, du rechnest gut, Tanja.

- Wieviel ist ....?
o Das ist leicht.

- Ich rechne gut, nicht?
o Ja, du rechnest gut.

- Komm, wir rechnen.
o Prima! Rechnen macht Spaß.

2 

Sag mal, wieviel ist drei mal dreißig?
Das ist schwer.
Drei mal dreißig ist ...
Das ist sehr schwer.

Überleg mal, Tanja.
Drei mal dreißig?
Drei mal dreißig, drei mal dreißig?
Ich weiß es. Neunzig.

Richtig.
Drei mal dreißig ist neunzig.

- Wieviel ist ....?

o Das ist schwer.
Ich weiß es nicht.

o Das ist leicht.
Ich weiß es.

1	10	2	20	3	30	4	40	5	50
eins	zehn	zwei	zwanzig	drei	dreißig	vier	vierzig	fünf	fünfzig

6	60	7	70	8	80	9	90
sechs	sechzig	sieben	siebzig	acht	achtzig	neun	neunzig

$A_2 \rightarrow Ü_1;KS_{15}$

3 Wir lesen

a. plus (+): Dreißig plus zwanzig ist fünfzig.

30 + 20 = 50	50 + 10 = 60	80 + 10 = 90
70 + 10 = 80	60 + 10 = 70	30 + 30 = 60
20 + 20 = 40	10 + 50 = 60	10 + 60 = 70

b. minus (−): Achtzig minus zehn ist siebzig.

80 − 10 = 70	90 − 30 = 60	40 − 30 = 10
90 − 50 = 40	80 − 20 = 60	70 − 40 = 30

c. mal (·): Zwei mal zehn ist zwanzig.

2 · 10 = 20	3 · 20 = 60	7 · 10 = 70
5 · 10 = 50	2 · 30 = 60	4 · 20 = 80

d. durch (:): Sechzig durch dreißig ist zwei.

60 : 30 = 2	70 : 10 = 7	60 : 6 = 10
80 : 20 = 4	40 : 20 = 2	70 : 7 = 10

+	plus
−	minus
·	mal
:	durch

LEKTION 

B

Zahlen

10 zehn
11 elf
12 zwölf
13 dreizehn
14 vierzehn
15 fünfzehn
16 **sech**zehn (!)
17 **sieb**zehn (!)
18 achtzehn
19 neunzehn

20 **zwanzig**
21 einundzwanzig
22 zweiundzwanzig
23 dreiundzwanzig
24 vierundzwanzig
25 fünfundzwanzig
26 sechsundzwanzig
27 siebenundzwanzig
28 achtundzwanzig
29 neunundzwanzig

30 **dreißig**
31 einunddreißig
32 zweiunddreißig
.. ..
40 **vierzig**
41 einundvierzig
.. ..
50 **fünfzig**
51 einundfünfzig
.. ..
60 ***sech*zig**
61 einundsechzig
.. ..

70 ***sieb*zig**
71 einundsiebzig
.. ..
80 **achtzig**
81 einundachtzig
.. ..
90 **neunzig**
91 einundneunzig
.. ..
100 (ein)hundert

Wir lesen

a sechs - sechzehn - sechzig - sechsundsechzig

b eins - einundzwanzig - einundneunzig

c sieben - siebzehn - siebzig - siebenundsiebzig

d zwei - zwölf - zwanzig - zweiundzwanzig

e drei - dreißig - dreizehn - dreiunddreißig

f vierzig - fünfzig - fünfzehn - vierzehn

g fünfundvierzig - vierundfünfzig - vierundvierzig - fünfundvierzig

h neunzehn - neunzig/siebzehn - siebzig/fünfzehn - fünfzig/dreißig - dreizehn/vierzig - vierzehn

B → $Ü_3$;AH_{1-8}

C

Wo wohnst du? Und dein Freund/deine Freundin?

Peter: *Wo wohnst du, Hans?*
Hans: *In Hamburg.*
Peter: *Und wo in Hamburg?*
Hans: *Milchstraße 13. Und du?*
Peter: *Auch in Hamburg, Binderstraße 24.*
Hans: *Hast du Telefon?*
Peter: *Ja. Meine Nummer ist 6-9-0-3.*

Susi Meier
Düsseldorf
Oststraße 33

Freundin:
Bastionstraße 17
Telefon (Susi):–

Ulrich Tacke
Köln
Lindenstraße 16

Freund:
Lindenstraße 41
Telefon (Ulrich):
2-0-0-5-1

- Wo wohnst du?
o (In der) Lindenstraße 16.

- Hast du Telefon?
o Ja. Meine Nummer ist ...   o Nein.

C → $Ü_2$;KS_{16}

LEKTION 

Ich möchte 

1

Peter: *Ich möchte einen Filzstift.*
Verkäuferin: *Hier bitte.*
Peter: *Und ein Heft und eine Postkarte. Was macht das zusammen?*

Verkäuferin: *Ein Heft 0,30, ein Filzstift 0,70, eine Postkarte 0,30. 1,30 bitte.*

0,30 DM = dreißig Pfennig.
1,30 DM = eine Mark dreißig.

100 Mark 50 Mark 20 Mark 10 Mark

1 Pfennig 2 Pfennig 5 Pfennig 10 Pfennig 50 Pfennig 1 Mark 2 Mark 5 Mark

2 Was möchtest du?

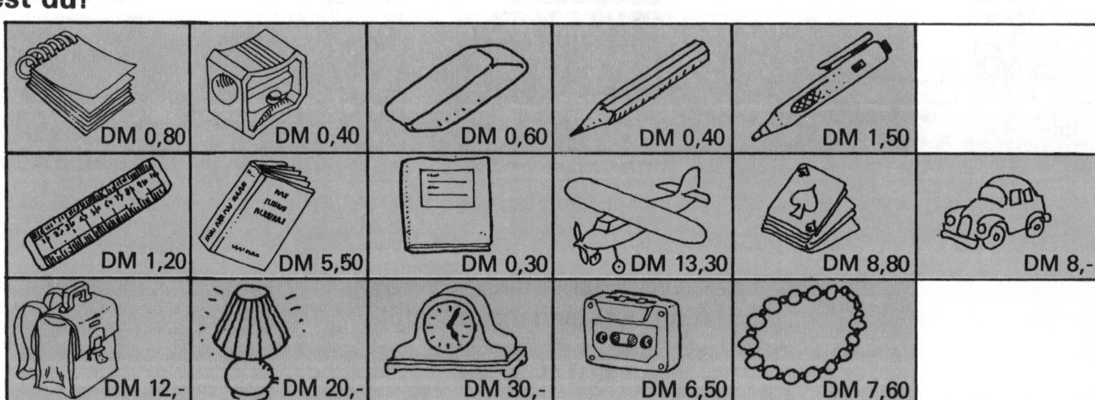

Ich möchte						
einen	DM 0,80	DM 0,40	DM 0,60	DM 0,40	DM 1,50	
ein	DM 1,20	DM 5,50	DM 0,30	DM 13,30	DM 8,80	DM 8,-
eine	DM 12,-	DM 20,-	DM 30,-	DM 6,50	DM 7,60	

Was macht das (zusammen)?

$D_1 \rightarrow Ü_4$;AH_{9-10};$D_2 \rightarrow KS_{17}$

1 Ist das schwer oder leicht?

1

2

3

4

5

6

7

8

2 Wir machen Interviews mit ...

Hans Hausmann
Bonn
Poststraße 77
Freund: Poststraße 5a
Telefon (Hans): 5-5-6-6

Birgit Buck
Freiburg
Schiffstraße 16
Freundin: Schiffstraße 26
Telefon (Birgit) 2-7-3-0

Heiko Schäfer
Frankfurt
Ganghoferstraße 21
Freund: Anzengruberstraße 14
Telefon (Heiko): –

Ina Scholz
Bremen
Ringstraße 33
Freundin: Ringstraße 1
Telefon (Ina): 7-5-7-5

3 Peter, wie alt ist dein/deine ...?

4

Norbert Neugierig

a)

1. Wie heißt du?
2. Wo wohnst du?
3. Hast du Brüder und Schwestern?
4. Hast du einen Hund? / eine Katze?
5. Was machst du gern?
6. Macht Spielen Spass?
7. Ist Turnen schwer?
8. Wann hast du Geburtstag?
9. Bekommst du auch Geschenke?
10. Was möchtest du denn gern haben?

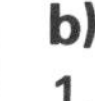

b)

1. Was kostet das Flugzeug?
2. Ist das ein Geschenk?
3. Wer bekommt das Geschenk?
4. Hat dein Freund Geburtstag?
5. Wo wohnt er?
6. Hat er Geschwister?
7. Hat er Tiere?
8. Was brauchst du zuerst?
9. Und jetzt?
10. Wie schreibst du? Nimmst du den Füller oder den Kuli?
11. Ist die Briefmarke richtig?

10

GRAMMATIK
KNACKER
Knacker knackt jede Nuß!

1 Rechnen

2 + 3 = ?	Wieviel ist zwei	plus	drei?	Zwei plus drei **ist** ......
6 – 3 = ?	sechs	minus	drei?	
2 · 6 = ?	zwei	mal	sechs?	
12 : 6 = ?	zwölf	durch	sechs?	

⚠→ **Wie viele** Kinder ...?

2 Zahlen (10 – 100)

Siehe Seite 116.

3

Wie	heiß	t	du?
Ich	heiß	e	Jens.
Wie	heiß	t	das auf deutsch?
Ich	weiß	-	es nicht.

Wann	komm	st	du?
Ich	komm	e	morgen.

4

Ich habe
bekomme
brauche
möchte
nehme

der - ein	das - ein	die - eine
einen keinen meinen deinen	ein kein mein dein	eine keine meine deine
Füller usw.	Buch usw.	Kette usw.

A

Ich habe keine Lust./Das macht Spaß.

LEKTION 11

Was machen wir jetzt?

Wir rechnen.

Nein. Ich habe keine Lust. [-]

Wir malen.

Malen. Immer malen.
Das ist doch langweilig! [-]

Ich habe eine Idee.
Wir basteln.

Prima! Das macht Spaß. [+]

B

Ham- pel-mann Ham- pel-mann Ham- pel Ham- pel- Ham- pel-mann

1

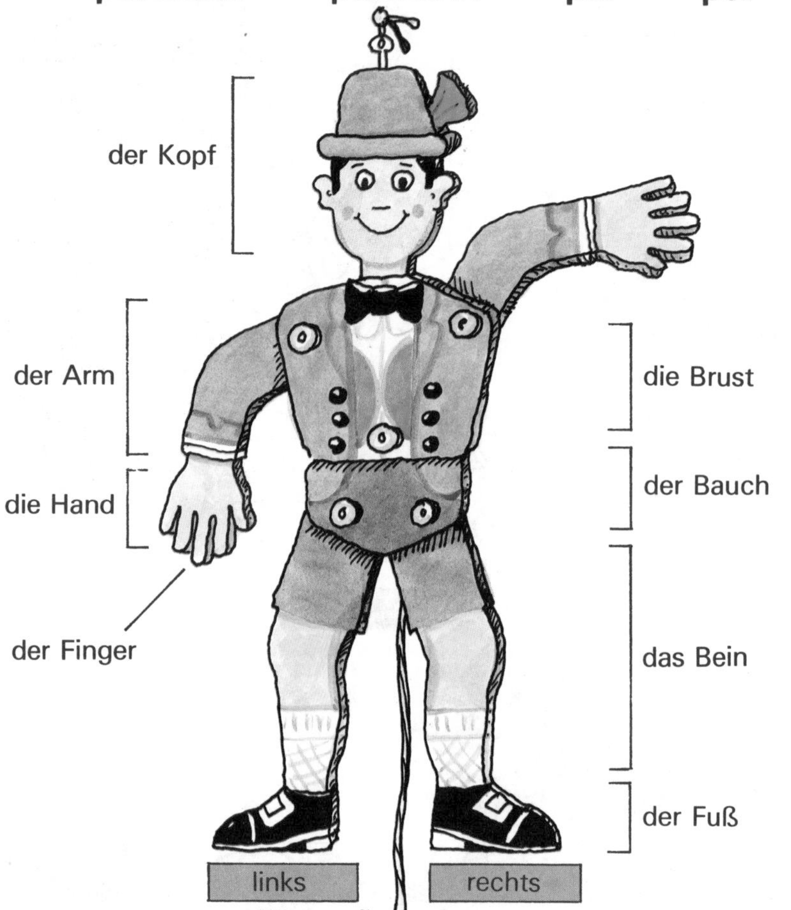

der Kopf

der Arm

die Hand

der Finger

die Brust

der Bauch

das Bein

der Fuß

links rechts

oben

in der Mitte

unten

Körperteile

der Kopf	ein ...	---
der Arm	ein ...	zwei Arme
die Hand	eine ...	zwei Hände
der Finger	ein ...	fünf Finger

die Brust	eine ...	---
der Bauch	ein ...	---
das Bein	ein ...	zwei Beine
der Fuß	ein ...	zwei Füße

Hier ist/sind ....
Zuerst kommt...........
Dann kommt ....
Zuletzt kommt ....

Oben ist ....
In der Mitte ist ....
Unten ist ....

A → $Ü_{1-2}$;AH_1

2 Wo fangen wir an?
Oben oder unten?
Was kommt zuerst?
Und dann?

Und jetzt?
Was fehlt?
Und was kommt zuletzt?
Der Hampelmann ist fertig.

C Was fehlt auf Bild 1, 2, 3, 4, 5, 6?

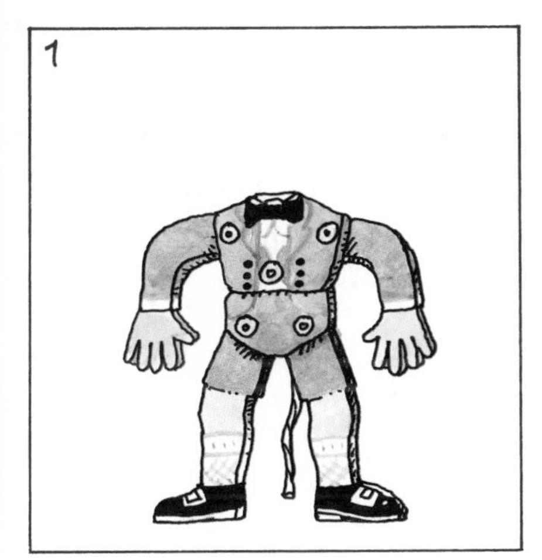

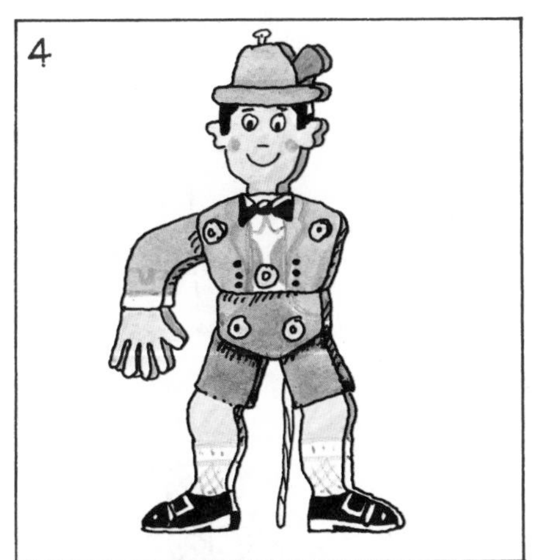

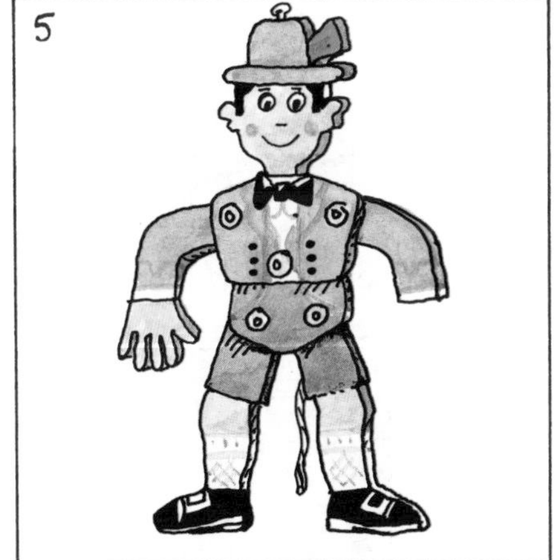

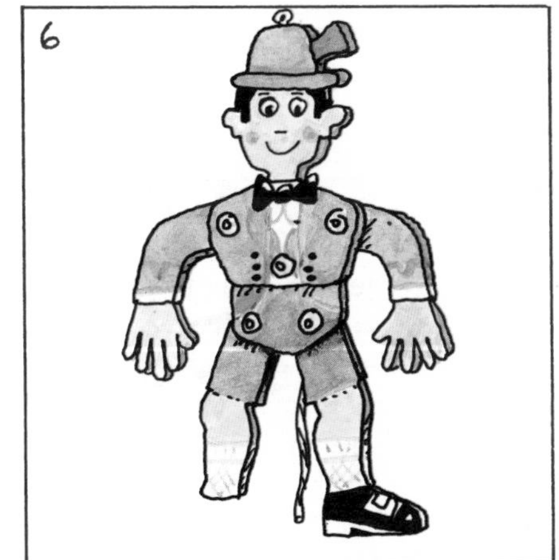

Bild 1: . . . . fehlt.
Bild 2: . . . .
Bild 3: . . . .
Bild 4: . . . .
Bild 5: . . . .
Bild 6: . . . .

B → $Ü_3$; AH_{2-5}; C → AH_6; KS_{18}

Und was fehlt jetzt?

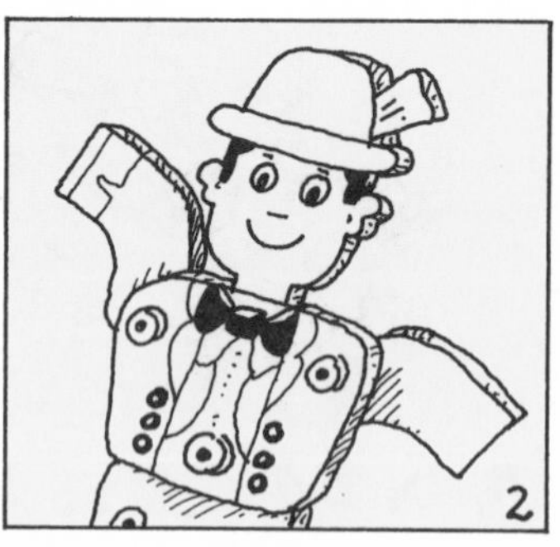

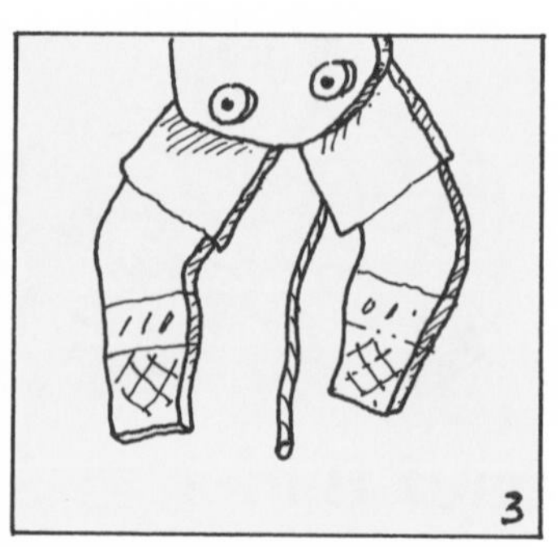

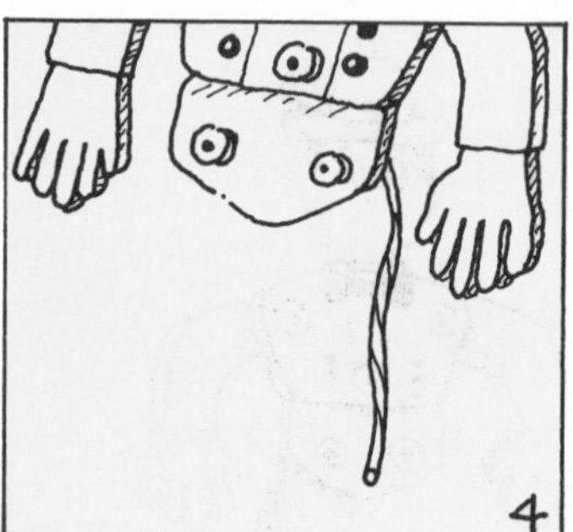

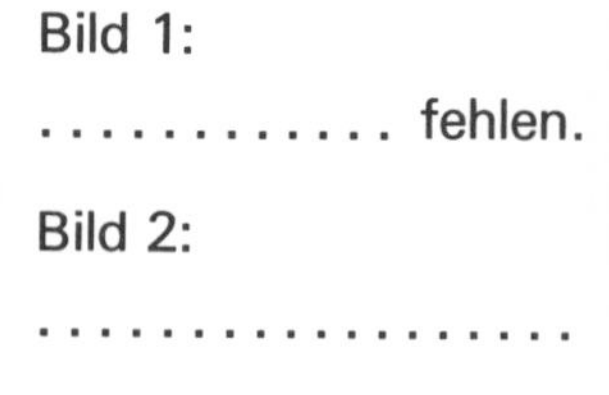

Bild 1:
.... fehlen.

Bild 2:
....

Bild 3:
....

Bild 4:
.... fehlen.

Bild 5:
....

Bild 6:
.... fehlt.

D Jetzt steigt Hampelmann

Jetzt steigt Hampelmann,
jetzt steigt Hampelmann aus seinem Bett her - aus.
Oh, du mein Hampelmann, mein Hampelmann, mein Hampelmann!
Oh, du mein Hampelmann, mein Hampelmann bist du!

2 Jetzt zieht Hampelmann, jetzt zieht Hampelmann seine Hose an.
3 Jetzt zieht Hampelmann, jetzt zieht Hampelmann seine Jacke an.

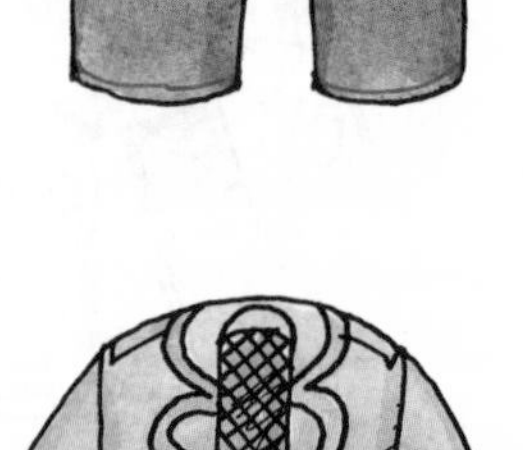

C → $Ü_4$;AH_7

Wir lesen 

Na so was!
Und wir haben keinen Regenschirm.

Und was machen wir jetzt zu Hause?

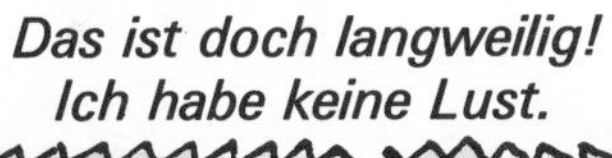

Das ist doch langweilig!
Ich habe keine Lust.

Kinder, ich habe eine Idee.
Wir basteln einen Hund.
Prima!

Komm, Sieglinde.
Ich mache ein Bild.

Wo sind denn die Beine,
Sigi?

Schau mal, hier.

1 Dialoge

Beispiel: - Komm, wir schwimmen.
o Nein, ich habe keine Lust.

Beispiel: - Komm, wir fahren Rad.
o Prima, das macht Spaß.

2 Dialoge

Beispiel:

- Liest du gern Asterix?

o Ja, sehr gern. Das macht Spaß. | o Nein, das ist doch langweilig!

a Asterix lesen
b basteln
c Briefe schreiben
d Bücher lesen
e Deutsch machen
f fernsehen
g Fußball spielen
h Hausaufgaben machen
i Klavier spielen
j malen
k radfahren
l rechnen
m reiten
n schlafen
o schwimmen
p turnen
g würfeln
r zu Opa und Oma gehen

3 Was ist hier falsch?

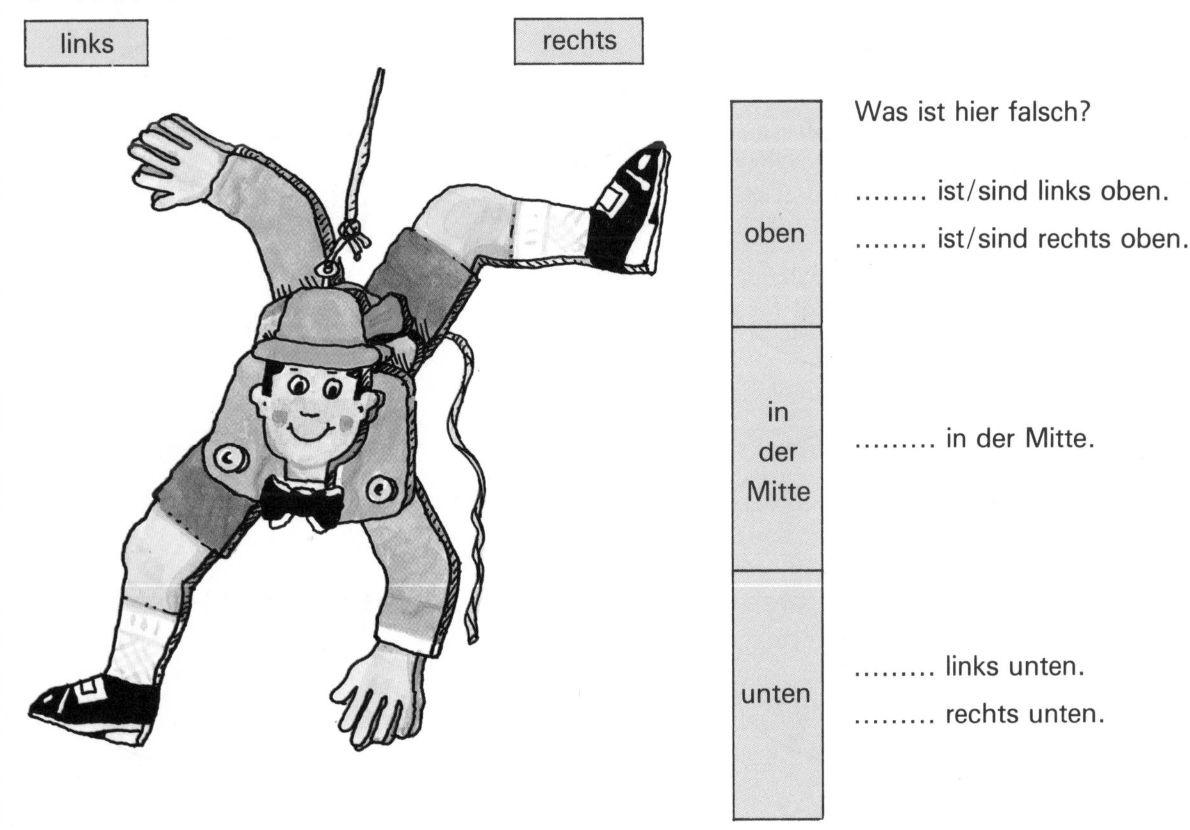

Was ist hier falsch?

.... ist/sind links oben.
.... ist/sind rechts oben.

.... in der Mitte.

.... links unten.
.... rechts unten.

4 Was paßt dazu?

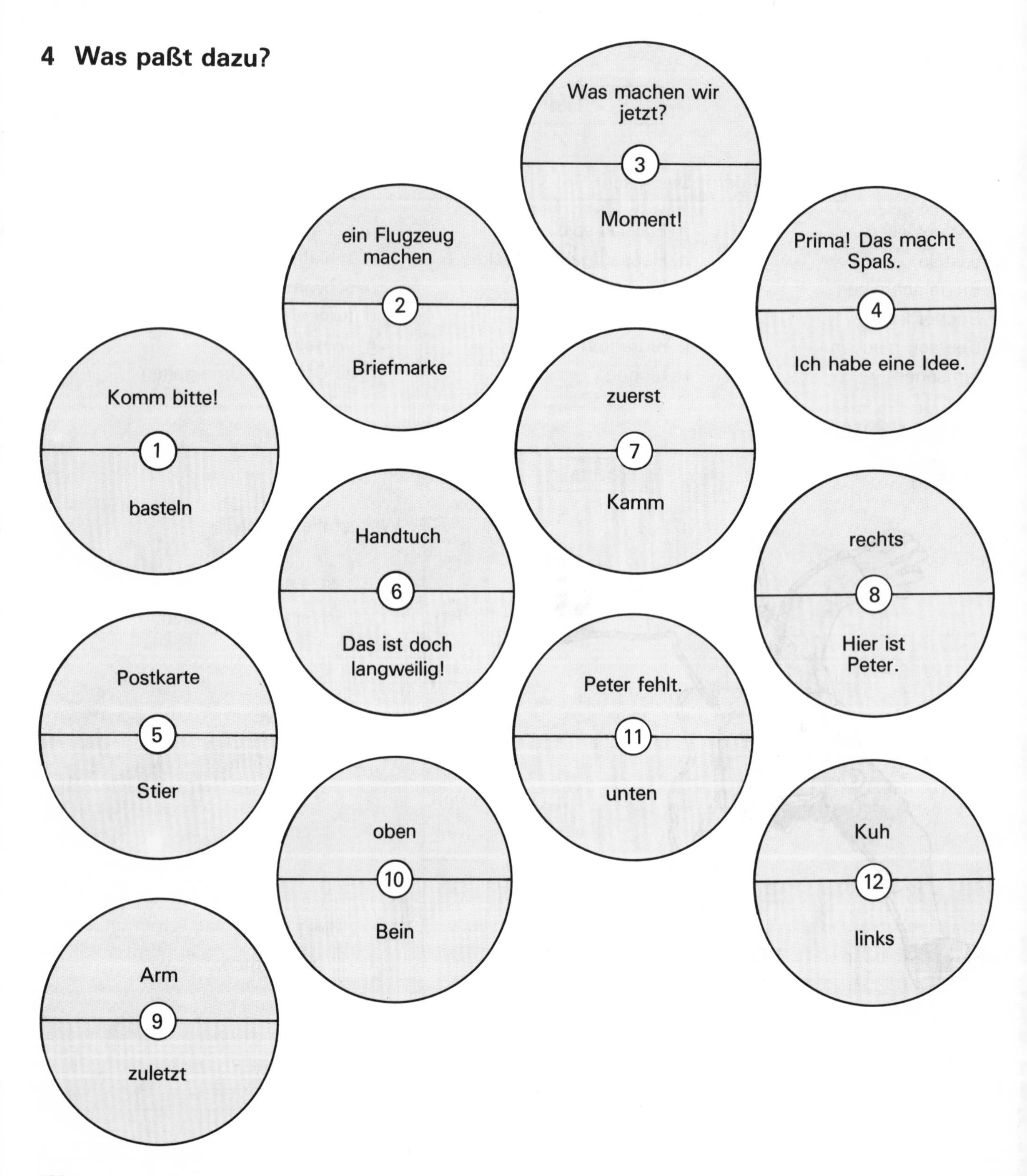

1		
	Der Kopf ist	oben.
	Der Bauch ist	in der Mitte.
	Das Bein ist	unten.
	Der Tisch ist	rechts.
	Die Tür ist	links.

2 Was fehlt?

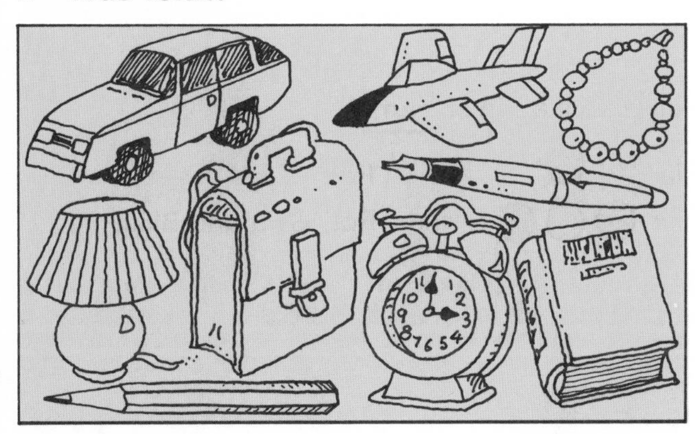

Der	Füller fehlt.	Das	Buch fehlt.	Die	Tasche fehlt.
ein - der		ein - das		eine - die	

3 Singular - Plural

Singular				Plural				
Hier	ist	ein	Arm.	Hier	sind	zwei Arme.		+ -e
		ein	Bein.			zwei Beine.		
Hier	ist	eine	Hand.	Hier	sind	zwei Hände.	a→ä	+ -e
Hier	ist	ein	Fuß.	Hier	sind	zwei Füße.	u→ü	+ -e
Hier	ist	ein	Buch.	Hier	sind	zwei Bücher.	u→ü	+ -er
Hier	ist	ein	Finger.	Hier	sind	zwei Finger.	-er	= -er
Hier	ist	eine	Kerze.	Hier	sind	zwei Kerzen.	-e	+ -n

SINGULAR PLURAL

4 Singular - Plural

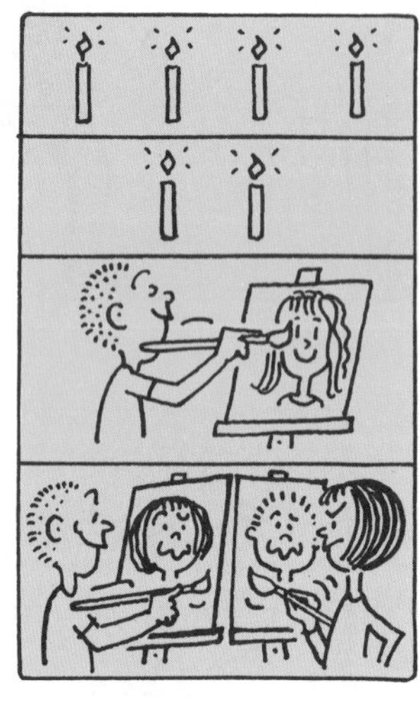

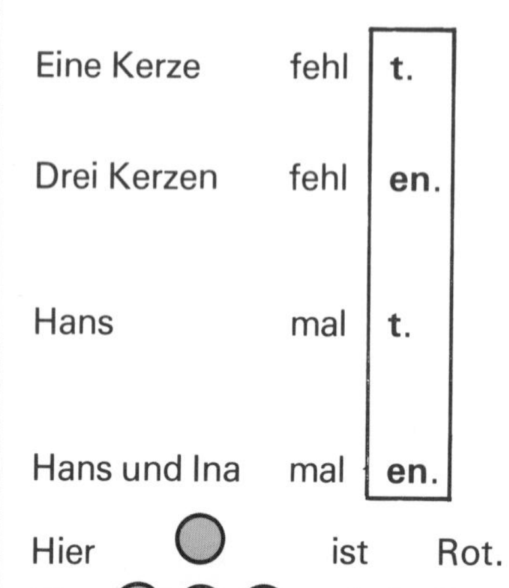

Eine Kerze	fehl	**t.**
Drei Kerzen	fehl	**en.**
Hans	mal	**t.**
Hans und Ina	mal	**en.**

Hier ● ist Rot.

Hier ● ● ● sind Rot, Gelb und Blau.

5 wir ...-(e)n

Wir schwimm	**en.**
turn	**en.**
bastel	**n.** (!)

6 Das hörst du in der Schule

Komm, wir schreiben.

Nein, ich habe keine Lust.

Wie heißt das auf deutsch?

Ich weiß es nicht.

Ich weiß es.

Komm, wir rechnen.

Immer rechnen. Das ist doch langweilig.

Ich habe eine Idee: wir basteln.

Prima! Das macht Spaß.

A

Kinder, seid nett zu Nina! 

1

Das ist Nina.
Sie ist neu hier.

Nina kommt aus Haan.
Das liegt bei Düsseldorf.

Sie wohnt jetzt
hier in Stuttgart.
Düsseldorf
Stuttgart

Nina, du kannst
bei Ursula sitzen.
Da ist noch ein Platz frei.

Kinder, seid nett zu Nina!

A → Ü$_{1a,2}$

2 Du bist der Lehrer. Was sagst du?

	Andreas	 Sandra	 Katrin	 Stefan
Woher kommt er/sie?	aus Starnberg	aus Fürth	aus Pforzheim	aus Lüneburg
Das liegt bei ...	 München	 Nürnberg	 Karlsruhe	 Hamburg
Wo wohnt er/sie jetzt?	  in Köln	 in Frankfurt	 in Bremen	 in Freiburg
Wo ist ein Platz frei?	 bei Christian	 bei Gero	 bei Bettina	 bei Ralf

- **Wo** wohnst du?
o In ... .

- **Woher** kommst du?
o Aus ... .

- **Wo** liegt das?
o Bei ... .

- **Wo** kann ich sitzen?
o Bei ... .

Kinder, seid nett zu ... !

3 Entschuldigung, ist hier die 3c? 

Nina: *Entschuldigung, ist hier die 3c?*

Arno: *Ja. Bist du neu?*

Nina: *Ja, ich bin neu hier.*

Arno: *Wie heißt du denn?*

Nina: *Nina.*

Arno: *Und woher kommst du?*

Nina: *Aus Haan.*

Arno: *Wo liegt das denn?*

Nina: *Bei Düsseldorf.*

Arno: *Ach so. Und jetzt wohnst du in Stuttgart?*

Nina: *Ja, jetzt wohne ich hier. Wo kann ich sitzen?*

Arno: *Bei Ursula. Der Platz dort ist frei.*

Nina: *Danke.*

Ebenso mit:

B

Nina auf dem Schulhof

1

Petra:
- *Wie alt bist du?*
- *Wann hast du Geburtstag?*

Ursula:
- *Wo wohnst du?*

Sabine:
- *Hast du einen Bruder?*
- *Hast du einen Hund?*
- *Hast du schon Freunde hier?*

Nina:
o *Ich bin neun Jahre alt.*
o *Im September.*
o *In der Bachstraße 37.*
o *Nein, eine Schwester.*
o *Ja, einen Hund und einen Hamster. Hier.*
o *Nein, noch nicht.*

Du bist neu in der Klasse 3c.
Was sagst du zu Petra, Ursula und Sabine?

2 Was sagen die Kinder?

$B_1 \rightarrow Ü_{1b,3}$

Wir gehen schwimmen. Kommst du mit?

Petra	Nina
Kannst du schwimmen, Nina?	*Ja. Warum?*
Wir gehen heute schwimmen. Kommst du mit?	*Ja, gern. Wann denn?*
Um drei. Du kommst zu mir. Ich wohne (in der) Königstraße 66.	*Ist das weit?*
Nein, das ist nicht weit.	*Also gut. Um drei.*

- Kannst du schwimmen?

o Natürlich.
Ja.
Ja. Warum?

o Nein.

- Wir gehen schwimmen. Kommst du mit?

\+

o Ja, gern, wann denn?
. . . .
- Also gut. Um ...

–

o Nein. Ich habe keine Lust.
Nein. Ich habe keine Zeit.
Nein. Ich kann heute nicht.

- Komm zu mir.
Du kommst zu mir.

Ich wohne (in der) Königstraße 66.

C → $Ü_{4-5}$;AH_{1-4};KS_{19}

Wir lesen

Susi Schlaksig

Morgen ist Samstag. Susi ist Samstag nicht gern zu Hause.
Was mache ich bloß morgen?
Hallo, Petra. Was machst du morgen?
Morgen? Ich gehe zu Hans.

Guten Tag, Stefanie. Ich gehe morgen schwimmen. Kommst du mit?
Warum? Was machst du denn?

Tut mir leid. Ich kann nicht.
Ich gehe zu Hans. Er hat morgen Geburtstag.

Guten Tag, Jens. Was machst du morgen? Kommst du zu mir? Wir können basteln.
Aber morgen gehe ich zu ...
Du gehst auch zu Hans? Na so was ...
Aber hör mal, Susi, ich ...

Was kann ich machen? Ja, ich habe eine Idee. Ich ...

Hallo, Hans! Hier ist Susi. Wir gehen morgen schwimmen. Kommst du mit?
Tut mir leid, Susi. Morgen habe ich hier eine Party. Kommst du nicht zu mir?

Wie? Eine Party?
Ich habe Geburtstag. Das weißt du doch!

Nein. Du hast Geburtstag?
Ja. Die Party ist um vier Uhr. Komm doch auch!
Ja, gern. Also morgen um vier. Auf Wiedersehen!

1a Nina in der 3c

a Woher kommt Nina? ....
b Und wo liegt das? ....
c Ist Nina schon lange hier? ....
d Wo kann sie sitzen? ....
e Der Lehrer sagt: ,,Kinder, seid ....''

1 Nina auf dem Schulhof

a Wie alt ist Nina? ....
b Wann hat sie Geburtstag? ....
c Wo wohnt sie in Stuttgart? ....
d Hat Nina eine Schwester? ....
e Hat sie auch einen Bruder? ....
f Hat Nina Tiere? ....
g Hat sie Freunde in Stuttgart? ....

2 Was paßt?

1	2	3	4

1

2

3

4

a
- Entschuldigung, ist dort noch ein Platz frei?
o Ja, du kannst hier sitzen.

b
- Komm, wir malen.
o Immer malen. Das ist doch langweilig!

c
- Herr Scholz, darf ich auch malen?
o Ja, natürlich. Da.

d
- Ich rechne gut, nicht?
o Ja, du rechnest sehr gut.

3 Wir fragen

- ....?
o *Ich heiße Nina.*

- ....?
o *Ich wohne jetzt in Stuttgart.*

- ....?
o *Ich komme aus Haan.*

- ....?
o *Ich sitze bei Ursula.*

- ....?
o *Nein, eine Schwester.*

- ....?
o *Ja, ich habe einen Hund.*

- ....?
o *Ja, ich habe auch einen Hamster.*

4 Kannst du ... ?

Du antwortest: Ja, natürlich oder Nein.

5 Was fehlt?

Hans:
Ich ... heute turnen.
... du mit?
Klaus:
Ja, ... denn?
Hans:
Um fünf.
Du kommst zu mir.
Klaus:
Wo ... du denn?
Hans:
Bachstraße 66.

Klaus:
Ist das ...?
Hans:
Nein, das ist nicht weit.
Klaus:
Also ... . Um fünf.

12 GRAMMATIK

KNACKER

Knacker knackt jede Nuß!

1 ist + Adjektiv

Mein Füller	ist	leer.	
Dein Teddy	ist	schön.	
Nina	ist	neu	hier.
Das	ist	leicht.	
Das	ist	schwer.	
Der Platz	ist	frei.	
		Adjektiv	

2 wo? und woher?

	Wo	wohnst du?
	In	Offenbach.
	Wo	liegt das?
	Bei	Frankfurt.
	Wo	ist dein Platz?
Hier	bei	Ursula.

Woher	kommst du?
Aus	Hamburg.

3

a

Wo	kann	ich	sitzen?	= darf
Du	kannst	bei Ursula	sitzen.	

b

Peter	kann		schwimmen.
Hans	kann	nicht	schwimmen.
Und du?	Kannst	du	schwimmen?
			Infinitiv

Komm, Hans!

Ich kann nicht schwimmen.

2M

4

Ich	gehe	heute	schwimmen.	Kommst du mit?

5

Ich	gehe	heute nicht	zu Petra.
Petra	kommt	heute	zu mir.

A

1 Versteckspiel: Wer hat die Katze?

2 Wir spielen Karten.

Du fragst: Hast du ...

den	das	die
Fisch	Kamel	Maus?
Tiger	Pferd	Kuh?
Esel	Lama	Gans?
Frosch	Schaf	Ziege?
....	....	.... ?

ein einen	Das ist Ich male	ein einen	Fisch. Fisch.	Hast du	Der den	Fisch schwimmt. Fisch?	der den
ein ein	Das ist Ich male	ein ein	Kamel. Kamel.	Hast du	Das das	Kamel ist braun. Kamel?	das das
eine eine	Das ist Ich male	eine eine	Maus. Maus.	Hast du	Die die	Maus ist grau. Maus?	die die

$A_2 \rightarrow Ü_1$;AH_1

B

Was braucht ... für die Schule? Was braucht er/sie nicht?

1 Jens/Anna braucht den .../das .../die ... (nicht).

2 Möchtest du den/das/die hier?

Ebenso mit:

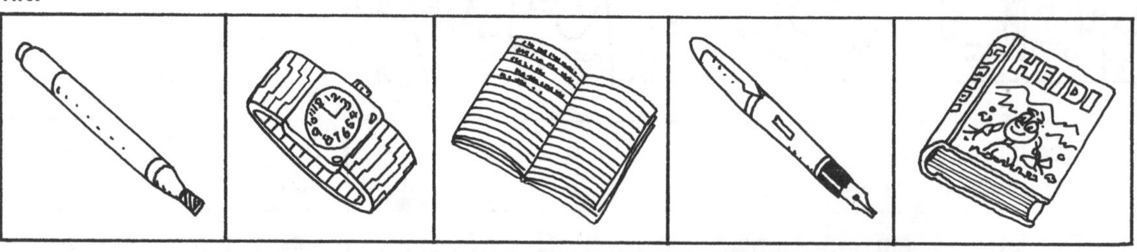

- Ich möchte	einen ...	ein ...	eine ...	.
- Möchtest du	den (...)	das (...)	die (...)	hier?
- Ja,	der	das	die	ist gut.

B → $Ü_2$;AH_2;KS_{20}

C

Was hat ...

1

Anna hat eine Bluse und einen Rock an.
Klaus ...., ...
Herr Adams hat ...., ... und .... an.
Er hat auch .... um.
Dirk hat .... und .... an.
Er .... auf und .... um.
Frau Adams .... an und .... auf.
Und was hast du an/ auf/ um? Dein Freund/ deine Freundin? Dein Lehrer/ deine Lehrerin? Deine Mutter? Dein Vater?

LEKTION 

3 Was zieht ... an?/ bindet ... um?/ setzt ... auf?

das Kleid

Sie zieht ein Kleid an.

Sie hat ein Kleid an.

1 : Der Junge zieht .... an .
2 : Das Mädchen ....
3 : Der Mann ....
4 : Der Junge setzt .... auf .
5 : Das Mädchen bindet .... um .
6 : Der Mann .... um .

Was ziehst du gern an? Was nicht?
Und dein Bruder/deine Schwester? Dein Freund/deine Freundin/dein Lehrer? Deine Mutter/dein Vater?

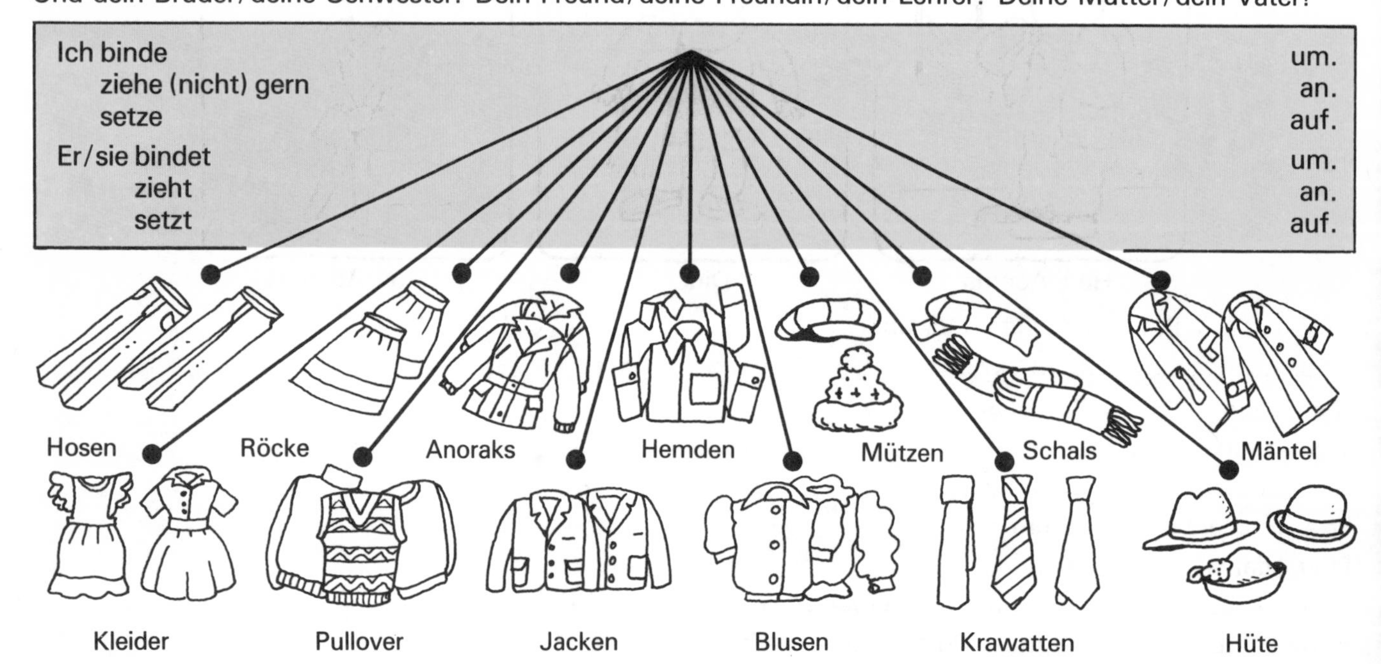

C → AH_{3-6}

Wir lesen und spielen

1

Was möchte der Junge zuerst? Und dann? Und dann? ... Und zuletzt?

2 Wir spielen die Geschichte noch einmal mit Schulsachen und Kleidungsstücken:

Gib mir ...

Gib mir	*den ...* *einen ...*	*das ...* *ein ...*	*die ...* *eine ...*

Wir lesen u. spielen 2 → $Ü_3$;AH_7;KS_{21-22}

Wir lesen 

Susi Schlaksig

BRAVO!
BRAVO!

Wie machst du deine Lieder?
Ich mache natürlich den Text selbst ...

... ich mache die Musik natürlich auch selbst ...
... und ich klatsche natürlich auch selbst.

Bravo! Noch einmal! BRAVO!
BRAVO! Noch einmal! BRAVO!

1 Wer hat die Katze?

- Wer hat die Katze?
o Peter.
usw.

2 Was bekommt ...

- Was bekommt Peter?
o Er bekommt das Spiel.
usw.

3 Gib mir bitte ...... !

GRAMMATIK

KNACKER

Knacker knackt jede Nuß!

1

Das ist	ein	Fisch.		Der	Fisch schwimmt.
Ich male	einen	Fisch.	Hast du	den	Fisch?
Das ist	ein	Kamel.		Das	Kamel ist braun.
Ich male	ein	Kamel.	Hast du	das	Kamel?
Das ist	eine	Maus.		Die	Maus ist grau.
Ich male	eine	Maus.	Hast du	die	Maus?

2

Ich möchte	einen Kamm	ein Buch	eine Kassette	.
Möchtest du	den (Kamm)	das (Buch)	die (Kassette)	hier?
Ja,	der ---	das ---	die ---	ist gut.

3

Er hat	einen Pullover	ein Hemd	eine Hose an.

4

Gib mir	den Pullover	das Hemd	die Hose!

5 Singular - Plural

Singular	Plural	
der Mantel	Mäntel	a → ä
der Rock	Röcke	o → ö + -e
das Hemd	Hemd**en**	+ -en
die Jacke	Jack**en**	+ -n
die Hose	Hos**en**	
die Bluse	Blus**en**	
die Krawatte	Krawatt**en**	
der Anorak	Anorak**s**	+ -s
das Kleid	Kleid**er**	+ -er
der Pullover	Pullov**er**	-er = -er

LEKTION 14

A

Herr Meier kann nicht schlafen

...6...7...8...

...99...100...101...102

hundert | hunderteins | hundertzwei

...9001...9002...9003

neuntausendeins | neuntausendzwei | neuntausenddrei

...9101...9102...9103

neuntausend einhunderteins | neuntausend einhundertzwei | neuntausend einhundertdrei

...32571...32572... So ein Mist...!

zweiunddreißigtausend-fünfhunderteinundsiebzig

zweiunddreißigtausend-fünfhundertzweiundsiebzig

B

Zahlen

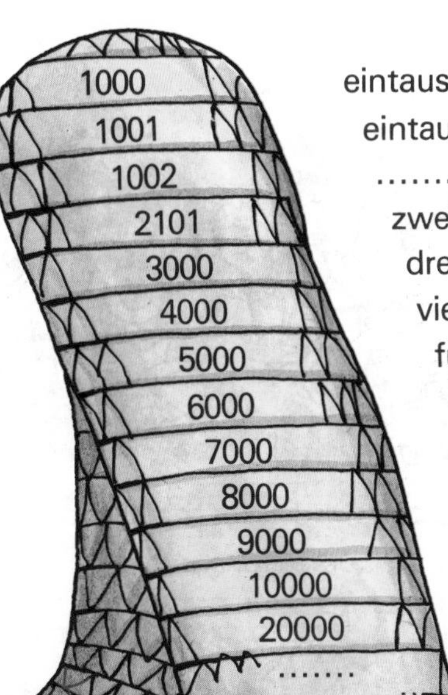

100	(ein)hundert
101	(ein)hunderteins
102	................zwei
201	zweihunderteins
301	dreihunderteins
400	vierhundert
500	fünfhundert
600	sechshundert
700	siebenhundert
800	achthundert
900	neunhundert

1000	eintausend
1001	eintausendeins
1002	.............zwei
2101	zweitausend**ein**hunderteins
3000	dreitausend
4000	viertausend
5000	fünftausend
6000	sechstausend
7000	siebentausend
8000	achttausend
9000	neuntausend
10000	zehntausend
20000	zwanzigtausend
....	....
100000	hunderttausend
....	....
1000000	eine Million

Jahreszahlen

1000 tausend
1100 elfhundert
1200 zwölfhundert
1300 dreizehn ....
1400 vierzehn ....
1500 fünfzehn ....
1600 sechzehn ....
1700 siebzehn ....
1800 achtzehn ....
1900 neunzehnhundert
1984 neunzehnhundert-vierundachtzig

LEKTION 

Der Bayerische Marsch

Einundzwanzig, zweiundzwanzig,
Drei-, vier-, fünf-, sechs-, siebenundzwanzig,
Achtundzwanzig, neunundzwanzig, dreißig.
Ja so geht der bayerische Marsch, Marsch, Marsch,
Ja so geht der Knüppel übern
Einunddreißig, zweiunddreißig, usw.

1 Wie heißt das Wort?

2 Kannst du das lesen? Dann buchstabier mal!

a	e	i	o	u	ä	ö	ü
1	2	3	4	5	6	7	8

K1nnst d5 d1s 12s2n?

R3cht3g.

W32 he3ßt d5?

W4 w4hnst d5?

W4h2r k4mmst d5?

Was m7chtest d5?

W4 3st H2rr M8ck?

D2r B6r schl6ft.

3 Wer findet das Wort?

Beispiel:
- R-a-d?
o Nummer 3

1 Oktober	2 Haus	3 Rad
4 Auto	5 Spaß	6 Bleistift
7 Füller	8 Ball	9 Buch
10 nett	11 langweilig	12 ja
13 Tanja	14 Hausaufgaben	
15 Januar	16 Dezember	
17 Filzstift	18 grün	
19 Mutter	20 Schwester	
21 wann	22 Hund	23 November

4 Wie heißt das Wort?

1 Buchstabe Nummer 4 in "würfeln" ☐

2 Buchstabe Nummer 2 in "Haus" ☐

3 Buchstabe Nummer 1 in "haben" ☐

4 Buchstabe Nummer 6 in "Januar" ☐

5 Buchstabe Nummer 2 in "brauchen" ☐

6 Buchstabe Nummer 5 in "Hausaufgaben" ☐

7 Buchstabe Nummer 11 in "Deutschland" ☐

$D_3 \rightarrow AH_2$

a b c d e f g h i j k l m n o p q r s t u v w x y z
A B C D E F G
H I J K LMNO P
Q R S T U V W
X und Yp-si-lon Z. Juch-he!
Das ist das gan-ze A B C!

F

Ich möchte ein Buch haben 

1

Stadtbücherei Wuppertal
Mitglieds-Nr.:
Vorname: __________
Familienname: __________
Geburtstag: __________
Straße: __________
Wohnort: __________

Junge:

Ich möchte ein Buch haben.

Nein, ich bin zum ersten Mal hier.

Dirk.

Browarzyk.

Browarzyk.

B-r-o-w-a-r-z-y-k.

Frau:

Warst du schon einmal hier?

Wie heißt du?

Und der Familienname?

Wie bitte?

Wie schreibt man das?
Buchstabier mal bitte!

Wir setzen das Gespräch fort!

Mai 1972 .... ?

Paracelsusstraße 66 .... ?

Wuppertal. .... ?

2 Wir spielen die Szene mit:

Mieschendahl, Günter	Potthast, Gerda	Jaruszewski, Ilka
Februar 1970	April 1973	August 1971
Liegnitzer Straße 29	Dasnöckel 16	Freymannstraße 52
Wuppertal	Velbert	Schwelm

$F_2 \rightarrow KS_{23}$

3 Suche die Reime.

A B C	1	b
D E F	2	
G H I	3	
J K L	4	
M N O	5	
P Q R	6	
S T U	7	
V W X	8	
Y und Z	9	

a Das reime ich auf 'Treff'.
b Peter trinkt gern Tee.
c Was möchten Sie, mein Herr?
d Tanja ist sehr fix.
e Hier steht eine Kuh.
f Jetzt gehen wir ins Bett.
g Heute bin ich froh.
h Peter hält das Knie.
i Hasso, komm und bell!

G Noch ein Gedicht

ABC

ABC
Der Hase sitzt im Klee.
DE
FGH
Der Hase sitzt noch immer da.

IK
Wer kommt da?
L
So schnell?
M und N
Das ist einer, den ich kenn!

O
Der Hase lief davo ...
PQ
RST
UVWXY
Der Has' lief wie der Blitz davon.

,,Oh, wenn ich ihn hätt!''
ruft der Fuchs.
Z.

$F_3 \rightarrow Ü_{1-3}; AH_{1,3-4}$

1 Was fehlt?

- Ich ... ein Buch haben.
o ... du schon einmal hier?
- Nein, ich bin zum ... ... hier.
o ....?
- Jens.
o ....?
- Domurath.
o Wie ....? ...... bitte!
- D-o-m-u-r-a-t-h.

o ....?
- Zehn Jahre.
o ... hast du Geburtstag?
- ... Februar.
o ....?
- In Düsseldorf.
o Und ... in Düsseldorf?
- Oststraße 26.

2 Was paßt?

3 Was paßt nicht?

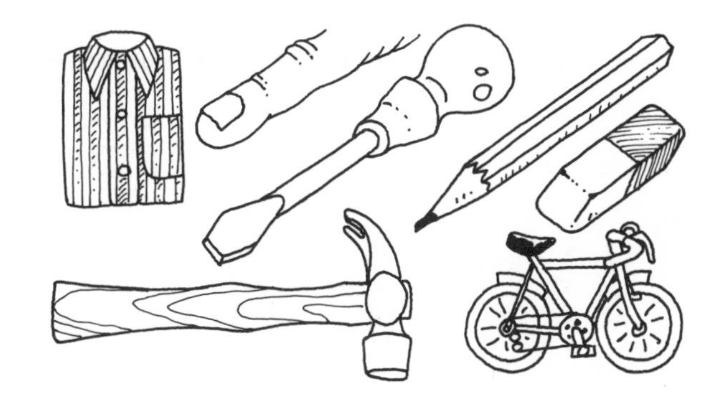

a Bauch, Brust, Hemd, Finger
b Schraube, Füller, Hammer, Schraubenzieher
c Kuli, Filzstift, Bleistift, Schreibmaschine
d malen, basteln, rechnen, würfeln
e Kette, Ventil, Fahrrad, Radiergummi

1985 Erste Auflage
1988 Zweite (Neue) Ausgabe
1990 Dritte Ausgabe
1990 Vierte Ausgabe
1991 Zweite Auflage

97 96 95 94 93
8 7 6 5 4

Für die Überlassung von Texten danken wir

Werner Halle — Wer ist dort,
aus: "Bilder und Gedichte für Kinder";
© Georg Westermann Verlag
Braunschweig 1976

Josef Guggenmos — Der Regenbogen,
aus: "Was denkt die Maus am Donnerstag";
© Georg Bitter Verlag
Recklinghausen 1967

Hildegard Wohlgemuth — Verkehrsschild,
aus: H.J. Gelberg (Hrsg.) "Die Stadt der Kinder";
© Georg Bitter Verlag
Recklinghausen 1969

ABC aus: "Die Liederkutsche";
© Hirschgraben Verlag
Frankfurt/Main

Richard Rudolf Klein — Der Hampelmann.
Grün, grün, grün sind alle meine Kleider.
Geburtstagstanz: Und wer im Januar Geburtstag hat.
Bruder Jakob
aus: "Willkommen, lieber Tag", Texte und Noten;
© Moritz Diesterweg Verlag
Frankfurt/Main 1975

Deutsche Bundesbank, Frankfurt/Main

Zahlenlotto — Westdeutsche Lotterie GmbH & Co., Köln

Für die Illustrationen danken wir

Colin Smithson, Richmond
John Wood, Leeds

Für die redaktionelle Mitarbeit an der Entwicklung von
Wer? Wie? Was? 1 danken wir James und Inge Moore.

C000184227

hear'say

OUR STORY

As told to Maria Malone

GRANADA

First published in Great Britain in 2001

By Granada Media, an imprint of André Deutsch Limited
20 Mortimer Street
London W1T 3JW

In association with Granada Media Group

A catalogue record for this book is available from the British Library.

ISBN 0 233 99998 1

Photographs Chapter 1 courtesy of Hear'say personal collections
Photographs pg 77, 78, 79 copyright © 2001 Ken McKay courtesy of Rex Features
Photographs pg 108 copyright © Matrix
Photographs pg 68, 69, 83, 109 © 2001 by David Tonge supplied courtesy of Idols Licensing and Publicity Limited
Photographs pg 116-119 copyright © Noel Sullivan
The Face cover reproduced courtesy of The Face. Cover photograph by Phil Poynter.
GQ cover © GQ/The Condé Nast Publications Ltd, photograph by Matthew Donaldson
The Sun front page reproduced courtesy of News International Syndication
All other photographs copyright © Granada Media Group Ltd, 2001

Special thanks to Simon Kenton at Idols for his kind assistance.
Photography for Chapter 5 and pgs 124–135 by Maria Malone
Photography pg 123 and 136–139 by Ken McKay

Project Editor Gillian Holmes
Design by Jonathan Lucas and Rachele Caltagirone
Managing Art Director Jeremy Southgate

Printed in Italy
10 9 8 7 6 5 4 3 2 1

Acknowledgements

Danny: There's only two simple and obvious words I can say – Thank you! I'd like to thank my whole family and close friends for their continued encouragement and support. Working on this book was like a therapy session – it made me look back and see how I managed to achieve something that seemed so far away. It also taught me you can never achieve anything on your own. Family and friends are so important – Mum, Nan, Granddad, Angie, Jamie, Billy and Grace – I love you. Chloe, thank you for your understanding. You are a special person. Hear'say crew – Myleene, Kym, Suzy and Noel, u know! Be lucky forever. Love, Danny.

Kym: I'd like to begin by thanking my parents, two very special people who have always supported me through good times and bad. Without you, I would never have fulfilled my dream I love you both. Also my brothers and sister, nieces and nephews, relatives and in-laws – thank you for putting up with me over the years. I love you all and miss you incredibly. My boyfriend Jack, for supporting me and helping me through some tough times recently. You are my rock and I love you! And last, but most importantly, my two babies David and Emily. You are the most important people in my life and you will always come first. Mummy loves you and misses you!! Until we are together again! So thank you all. Love ya and miss ya!!

Myleene: To the most important people in my life – my family. Mum, Dad, Chezzie and Dan. Taxi driving, satellite phone calls, 6 a.m. train dashes and, most importantly, your time. Than q. I love you very very much. Daughter Number 1. Ate x And Hear'say gang – Danny, Suzy, Noel and Marshy – Omigod! What are we doing? ... Whatever it is, keep on 'paddling.' Love you all. X

Noel: I hate this bit coz I need a book of my own to thank everyone who has helped me and is still helping me to realise my dream! Here goes ... Mama. Thank you. Words can't tell you any more, you know!!! My family, the strongest foundation to build my life upon – meme, Cath, Mark, Luke and Joel, I love you. My friends who have remained unchanged and fully supportive – thank you. And finally, Hear'say – Myleene, Suzy, Kym and Danny, I love you all and always will! We've had a laugh and a few tears but already we've built something together that no one can touch. Thank you for your support guys, you've been amazing. Love to all, Noel. X

Suzanne: BIG thanks to my family and friends for having faith. Thanks to my mum and to my dad. Thanks to Andrew, who has been there through the best and worst times. And to my new best friends and colleagues – I could not have wished for a better bunch. If my granddad can hear this, you hold a very special place in my heart. I love you and you will always be my Number 1 fan! Also, thanks to our fans for making this possible for us all. We couldn't have done this without you. Thanks guys! Love you all very much.

To the fans

Thank q is not enough. U guys r Hear'say – you know the score. Our love to Safe, Polydor and Granada and the Hear'say team – you make Hear'say fly. Than q is not a big enough word, so we'll just say it louder ... THAN Q! HEAR'SAY FOREVER.

From Maria

My love and heartfelt thanks go to the five people who have made it such a joy to be part of this book – Danny, Kym, Noel, Myleene and Suzanne. You are so good to know. Thank you for your time, your honesty, your humour, your trust ... and for always being your amazing selves. I am grateful to your families too for raiding the photo albums. I am also grateful to those who went out of their way to be helpful during the writing of *Our Story*, among them Tracy Watts and Tony Myers from Polydor Records, Grant Logan and the Safe Management team, and Paul Domaine. Thanks go to Vicki Stowe and Roseanne Boyle for their support, and to Susanna Wadeson for offering encouragement at just the right moment. Thanks too to my editor Gillian Holmes for remaining calm throughout. Finally, love to my family, and to June Taylor and Jo Turnbull for endless propping up. To those who held my hand throughout, my eternal gratitude.

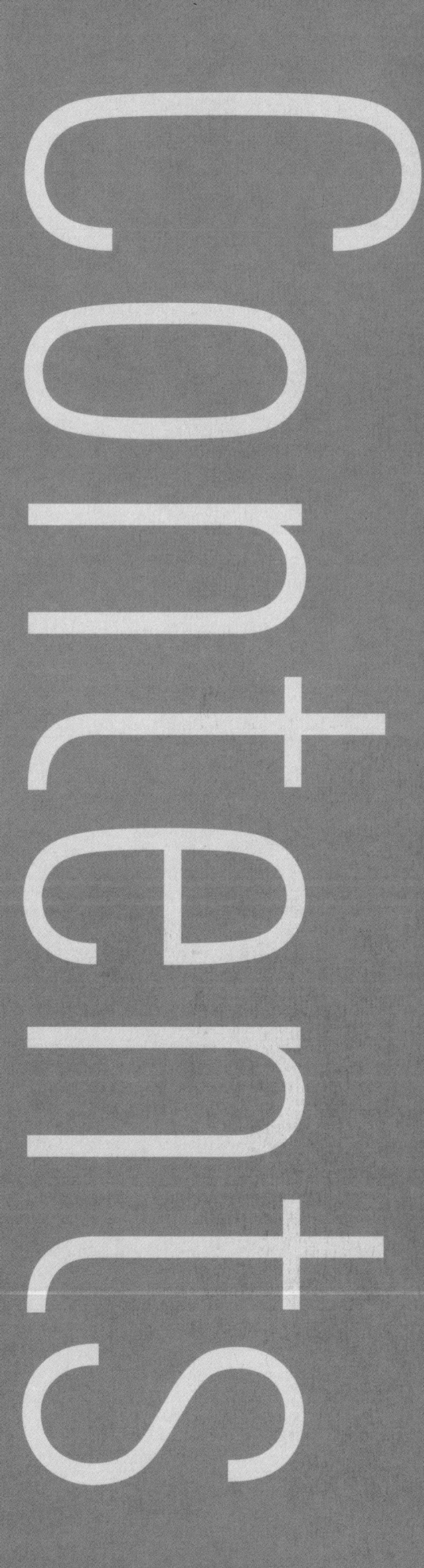

THE CHILDHOOD YEARS

1

Noel: 'I used to get name-called at school, and there was a bit of bullying, but I just thought that's what everyone got. I think I always knew I was going to do something good later on.'

1.1

DANNY'S STORY

Kym says: 'Danny is very strong, emotionally. When everyone else is down, he's up. He's always got a smile on his face and something positive to say. I get on very well with Danny – I class him as one of my best friends. I love him to pieces.'

'I suppose I had a really good childhood. It was just an average childhood for someone growing up in Hackney. My mum, Tracey, was sixteen and my dad, Dale, was eighteen when they had me, and it was probably not the best decision for them at the time. They were just far too young and there was a lot of pressure on them because it was a mixed-race relationship. I really don't know how my mum managed. I think initially it was probably a big shock to my family that she became pregnant so young, but once the shock wore off she had a lot of support from my nan and granddad, and that's how she got by. She probably couldn't have done it without them. I suppose in a way it's the same for Kym – she probably wouldn't be able to do this without her mum and dad, and that counts for a lot.

My mum and dad split up when I was really young, probably about two or three. My dad wasn't around much and the press put a spin on that, but there has never been any animosity. I wasn't really in touch with him, not on a regular basis, but I never felt, oh I haven't got a dad, or that I should be seeing him. It was kind of, if I do see him, fine, if I don't, fine. I used to go and stay with him at weekends, play football and stuff, and that was really good. We speak quite a bit but I don't feel the need to see him all the time. My relationship with my dad is fine.

I lived with my mum in a tower block in Hackney until I was ten and it was great. There were loads of kids in the same situation and I used to play out all the time. We'd play in the streets, climbing on roofs and just making our own entertainment. I always had such a lot of support from my mum and nan and granddad. We were such a big extended family. I never felt like I was missing out on anything at all. When you're a kid you're not aware of any struggle going on. I never really fussed about having loads of things or holding my hand out for money. I was always dressed nice, had nice birthday and Christmas presents, and never went without. We had a nice home as well. I don't know how my mum did it but she did, and it's not really 'til you get older and look back that you realize it's a real achievement.

When I was seven my mum had my sister, Jamie-Lee. She's got a different father from me. I remember the day my sister was born – I'd always wanted a baby sister. My nan was with my mum and I was with my granddad and when he told me I had a sister I cried. When she was a baby we had a lot of time together, even though we didn't always live in the same house. Now she's a teenager doing her thing and I understand that. We're close but not 100 per cent close. She's got Hear'say posters up but she's into garage music and what you might call cool things for a fourteen-

TIME CHECK

When Danny was born on 3 May 1979, Art Garfunkel was at number one with Bright Eyes year-old. I'm not sure Hear'say's that cool for her, and that's probably because her brother's in it. When something's that accessible you don't make a big thing of it. She's not like me at all, but then we've got different dads.

When I was ten my mum moved away because her relationship with my sister's dad had broken down. I was just about to start secondary school and I didn't want to move so I moved in with my nan. I'd say my nan and granddad were probably more lenient with me, not that my mum was ever really strict. But, say if I was off school because I was ill, then I wanted to play out at night, my mum would say, "If you're not well enough to go to school you're not well enough to play out." My nan would just say, "Oh, go on then!"

My mum only moved away for a little while, a few weeks, then she came back and moved into a block over the road. From my nan's house I could see my mum's, that's how close it was. My nan's house has always been a base for everyone – my mum's always there, my sister, my aunt, my cousins. People think that because I didn't live with my mum there must have been something wrong, or that because I didn't see much of my dad I couldn't have liked him, but that's just how it was. Everyone's life is different and I don't feel I was affected in a bad way by anything that happened. I just saw it as normal.

I think when I got into *Popstars* the press thought there had to be something wrong and they dug and dug, but anyone can see there are no problems at all. Even though I made a decision to live with my nan, my mum was there to support me, and I think it was the right decision. Maybe if I'd lived with my mum things would have been

You can see I was a happy baby!

I used to play out with my mates all the time.

1.1

Noel says: 'I think he has had a very similar life to me and that our personalities are quite similar. People imagine us to be very different, but actually we're very alike and we get on really well. The reason you become friends with people is because you see qualities in them you'd like to have and with Danny there are so many – he's very patient and a good listener. I feel like I've known him all my life.'

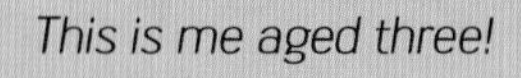

This is me aged three!

different. It's hard to explain, but even though my mum only lived over the road, her block was a totally different world. It was a bad area and there were some bad things going on – kids breaking car windows and staying out late and stuff. I never like to talk anyone down because a lot of people from there have done really well, but I think some people would have wanted to do more with their lives but got into a rut. They got into a gang and got into trouble and there were drugs and stuff. I've seen people my age, twenty-two, on drugs and that could so easily have been me because it was all around me. You'd see people on street corners doing dodgy things and I was aware of that. If I'd grown up there and kept in contact with the people I'd known when I was younger, my life would have been totally different – and I think my mum saw that. She put me in the right place, which was a brave thing to do.

People ask if I think that coming from a single-parent family gave me more drive and I always say no, but actually, I think it probably does. I saw friends having babies at sixteen, and you learn from that and decide not to go down that route. I know my mum wouldn't change me for the world, but she probably would have liked to have done a few more things before she'd had me, and you can accept that.

I loved school, although I remember my first day at nursery and I hated it! I think it was just the transition. Stability is quite important to me. Apparently Taureans don't like change. I just remember running round and this big black lady, with a woolly hat that looked like a tea cosy hanging on to me. Primary school was great. I kind of lived for it. I went to Thomas Fairchild, which was just over the road. I never saw school as a chore – it was just a good place to learn and have your social life.

Towards the end of primary school I did something really out of character and got into trouble. There was this boy who was a bit of a nutter and he was saying stuff about my mum. I just ran after him and chased him round the room. The teacher was telling me to stop, but I just kept going. As he ran one way, there was a chair in front of me and I picked it up and flung it across the room, which was really dangerous. I could have killed someone. I always remember two marks in the blackboard where the legs hit it – they'll be there for years. I had to go and sit outside the head's room and I think I had to do lines or something. The teachers knew what that boy was like but it still didn't justify me throwing a chair across the room.

I'm really close to my nan.

I got this bike for Christmas and it was wicked.

1.1

I was never naughty – well hardly ever.

Sometimes, when you grow up in London, you don't get to see anything outside that, like the seaside, but we used to go on trips to places like Devon. We'd do things like go canoeing, and it was wicked. I never felt deprived. My nan's mum had this caravan at Clacton-on-Sea – we've still got it – and we'd all go there in the summer holidays. They were some of the best times of my life. Without a doubt I had a happy childhood. Although my upbringing wasn't conventional, I wasn't aware of that. Looking back at my old photos you can see I was happy. I was always smiling. I know that being mixed-race is an issue for some people, but it wasn't until I got older that I really thought about it. People try and put you in a box – you're white or you're black – and because I grew up with my mum's side of the family they'd put me in the "white box". I've actually got a bit of both worlds, which is excellent. You also get a better grasp of how people are feeling with racism – a lot of the time it's down to ignorance but I've had the chance to learn from two cultures. I'd like to think that being mixed-race is a sign that barriers are being broken down.

I'd made a vow I wouldn't go to secondary school because I loved primary school so much. It's only when you go to secondary school that you realize how much work you have to do. I went to Central Foundation Boys School in Old Street and that was a daunting time. It's another milestone and everything changes again, but I actually loved it. It was just like any inner city school, a bit rough and ready, and all of us had to be strong. There was bullying, although luckily I never got bullied, but there was always banter going on. If it was your birthday there were beatings – you'd rush each other and beat each other up. It's stupid, not civilized at all, but it's just how boys communicate.

Suzanne says: 'I think he's the one who keeps us all together because he's such a strong lad. I admire the fact that each day is better than the one before for Danny – that's how he looks at life. He has a sensitive side. If you're upset he's there with a hug. I really look up to him.'

I think I decided from about Year 8 that I wanted to be a teacher. I always wanted to get decent grades. I don't know where that came from. Maybe it was because I enjoyed school so much and the teachers were cool. It was one of the happiest times for me. I was really into PE. I used to run and I've got medals for that. I was into athletics and basketball. I'd go to after-school clubs and I'd actually be in school from eight in the morning to nine at night. One of my mates, Avinash, lived in Golders Green, and the other, Wayne, lived in Clapham Common. That felt like a million miles away, so we'd hang about together after school.

A lot of people did muck about and loads of people from my primary school didn't have any interest in school whatsoever. I suppose a lot of people would rather bunk off than work, but I wanted to be a teacher so there was no way I could do that. In class I'd have a joke but I'd also do my coursework. Luckily, I came out with four Bs, four Cs and a D in my GCSEs. Looking back, I could have worked much harder. For a while I wanted to be a French teacher so I really knuckled down. We were with a tough examining board but I still got a B for French, and I was the only person in the school who got a grade in a language that year, so I was really proud of that.

When I heard I had a baby sister, I cried.

By the time I was about fifteen I could see loads of my mates doing stupid things – drugs, nicking car stereos, starting fires, just running about on the streets and getting chased by the police – so I put my energy into something positive and got involved in the local youth club.

I remember feeling like maybe I wasn't as cool as everyone else because I wanted to be a teacher and no one else around there wanted to do that. But I think people admired the fact that I wanted to do something and I was really going for it. They never saw me as a boffin or a swot. I could be down-to-earth but still do mad things if I wanted to. But I'd always go in at night and do my coursework instead of staying out 'til two in the morning, drinking cider, like some of my friends.

I stayed on at school for a year doing A levels – geography, media studies and technology – but I left because I wasn't enjoying it as much as I could have. It was an all-boys school and we were turning into young men, and I just felt I needed to socialize with girls as well. I decided to leave and do a diploma in childcare for two years, so I went to Islington College, and I loved it. There was a big stigma attached to doing that, because not many guys did it – I think there were five in total in the

Myleene says: 'Danny is such a clever guy, he can always see the bigger picture. If I want an unbiased opinion – and the correct opinion – Danny's the one to go to. He's a really fair person and so kind. He is the eternal optimist and has such a good sense of humour. Everyone thinks he's quiet but he's not. He's a beautiful guy.'

One of the rare occasions you'll ever see me in a shirt and tie – at my uncle's wedding.

Soaking up the sun on holiday with my granddad.

whole college. When you went into placements you had to be good and, luckily, I was. I got a distinction and I'm really proud of that.

It wasn't daunting that it was mainly girls. You've got to do what you want to do at the end of the day, so I never worried about it. I think there should be more male primary school teachers anyway – there are so many single-parent families around and in a lot of cases kids don't get to see their dads. I think it's important for them to see men in a positive role.

I had a conscious plan when I decided on the childcare course. I thought I'd have a qualification and be able to work if I wanted to and then do a degree later. Then I decided to have a year out and find my feet. I was singing and I wanted to see if I could succeed with that. You've got to live life with no regrets and be able to say you tried. I got a cleaning job, so I was working evenings and had the days free for auditions.

I'll never forget where I come from. I still live in Hackney now and I'm proud of it.

1.1

People think you should have some big house in Hampstead – well, I looked at Hampstead and I didn't like it. I still go down the pub with my nan and granddad because I'm a Hackney boy at heart. I'd like to think I'd be a positive role model for other kids who want to do things. Still, I have had my moments. I remember once I'd gone out for a drink, got really drunk, then went to a cheap eat-as-much-as-you-like grotty Chinese restaurant. I had lots and lots to eat, then went home, felt sick, ran down the stairs and spewed up all over the walls. As I got to the toilet I heard a big thud, came out – still drunk – and my nan was on the floor at the bottom of the stairs. She'd slipped on my sick and she had a huge bruise the next day. It was really embarrassing.

One of the few times I was able to be a little devil and get away with it.

While I was at college in 1998, I got really ill and nearly died. I thought I had flu but it was a bank holiday weekend so I thought I'd wait 'til the Tuesday to go to the doctor. I was being sick all weekend but I just carried on, although I wasn't really eating anything and I was really pale.

On the Sunday night I went to bed and in the middle of the night woke up being uncontrollably sick. I went to the toilet and collapsed. My granddad had to kick the door in to get to me. I don't really remember anything about it, but apparently I'd made so much noise running down the stairs to the bathroom I'd woken my nan and granddad. I didn't know it, but at that point I was close to dying. My heart was pumping like mad. I was taken to hospital by ambulance and by then I'd lost loads of blood, something like six pints. All weekend when I was being sick, I was losing blood, although I hadn't realized it. They told my granddad I was really lucky to be alive.

I spent the night in intensive care, having transfusions, but it felt like it was all happening around me. I was very weak and had to have oxygen, and I remember being taken onto the ward and my mum and my nan being there. That night I was really depressed. I'd nearly died and I didn't even know what was wrong with me. They did loads of tests and could never say for definite what it was. I was in hospital a week before they let me come home. What they thought was wrong was something called pylori – it's bacteria in your stomach and anyone can get it. Usually, you'd just have a bit of stomach trouble and that would be it. It was extreme in my case.

Afterwards, I did a lot of thinking. When you almost die it makes you think you really have to live, seize the day. I'd always been a focused person but that made me feel that when I got back to college I really had to get that distinction. I feel lucky to be alive. It was a big lesson about not taking things for granted.

Not long before that happened, my uncle Darren died of a heart attack in the same hospital. That was a shock. He was only twenty-seven and he had two kids – Grace who was about two and Billy who was around seven. Out of the blue one summer night I got a phone call saying he'd collapsed; I thought it was because of the heat. I remember running to get my nan and granddad. I was about fourteen at the time and I looked after the kids while they went to the hospital. You know when you think someone's coming back? He didn't. That was the first time I lost someone close, there was no warning, no medical condition that we knew about, nothing. He had a heart defect. That's just how life is. It was really hard for Angie, my aunt. Someone she loved was taken away from her. She copes really well, she's a great mother and a tower of strength.

Another close uncle, Jimmy, died later of leukemia. These experiences put things in context. But strangely, I'm not scared of dying. I think you're here to live your life and do good things. Coming close to death was probably one of the most important things that ever happened to me. I look back and think, "that was life-changing".

Anything I do now I never do half-heartedly, I do it properly. I read a book called *You Can Heal Your Life,* by Louise Hay, that taught me you can't look back, you can only learn from the past and live in the present. Reading that helped me understand a bit more about myself and about believing in myself. It taught me that all power is in the present and that every decision you make affects your life. It's about creating opportunities for yourself.'

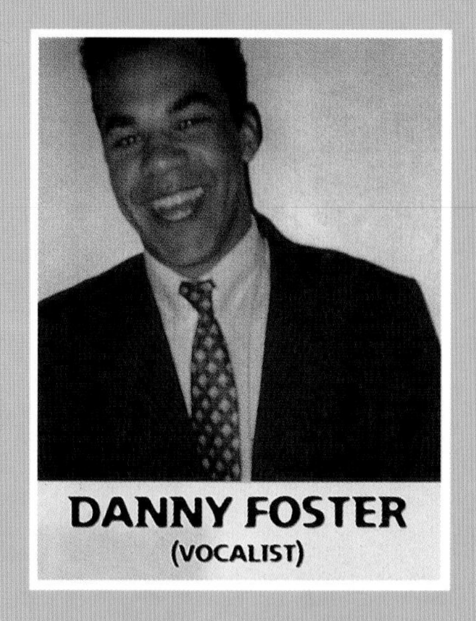

This was my publicity picture when I was doing pub singing.

With my mum on holiday in Clacton-on-Sea.

1.2 KYM'S STORY

Suzanne says: 'She is a fantastic singer and her kids come first – always. She's got a wise head on her shoulders. People think of her as being a very strong person but she's not. She needs a lot of attention and she doesn't always like being on her own. It's good she's got Jack now – you can see how happy she is.'

'I was the youngest of four kids and everyone thought I was a bit spoiled, and maybe I was. I used to get away with murder. I didn't really get on with my brothers, David and John, and my sister, Tracy, but we're really close now. I used to share a room with my sister and she'd constantly complain that I'd been in her stuff. My brother used to go mad if I went in his room, so I was always getting shouted at for that. They had to cope with this younger sister and it was probably a pain in the butt for them.

I was very close to my dad, David. He called me his shadow because I used to follow him everywhere. I was definitely daddy's girl. My dad is musical: he was in a band called Ricky and The Dominant Four, and his mum was a fantastic singer. She died when I was one so I don't remember her but, apparently, I used to sit on her knee and try to sing with her.

No one really knew I had any interest in singing or performing, although I started dance school when I was three – ballet, tap, modern, jazz – and did well in competitions. I remember once I told my mum, Pauline, that I was running away from home and all I packed were my dance shoes and some chocolate! I enjoyed dancing but I knew it wasn't what I really wanted to do. There was something else – I just wasn't sure what it was.

When I was ten we went to a local Labour club where everyone was getting up and singing with the resident band. I begged my dad to let me have a go. He put me off and said maybe the next week. A week later I got up and sang the Cliff Richard song "Living Doll". Everyone's mouths just dropped open; they couldn't believe it. Someone came over to my parents and suggested I join the Starlight Roadshow, which was a group of kids that did charity shows, so I did. That was my first audition, which was a bit nerve-racking. I sang "99 Red Balloons". After my audition they put me straight into a show. I had a boob tube on that kept falling down, so all through the song I was hitching it up. It was hilarious. The other kids were really nice, really talented.

We played at the Liverpool Garden Festival and the Floral Pavilion at New Brighton and when I was eleven I performed Whitney Houston's "Greatest Love Of All" and won the Ken Dodd Trophy. I also got the part of Kate in the musical *Annie* at the Liverpool Empire. We had rehearsals twice a week and I really looked forward to them. When I wasn't at rehearsals I was singing at home. My dad had bought me

Here I am looking exactly the same as my daughter Emily looks now.

Me with my mum and aunty Carroll.

a karaoke machine and he made sure I practised every day at a certain time. Without that discipline I don't think I'd be where I am today.

We lived in a semi-detached dormer bungalow in Garswood, in Lancashire. It was a lovely house, and Garswood was a beautiful place to grow up. There were lots of kids around. My best friend, Tricia, lived about five doors away. Everyone fancied a boy called Ian Mills. We went out for a while and my first kiss was with him outside my mum's house. He put his mouth round mine and it was horrible – it was all slobbery. I went in the house and wiped my face.

We lived there until I was ten and then we had to move because my dad's joinery business went into liquidation through no fault of his own. He took on a big job and the firm he was doing the work for went bankrupt. We lost our house and that was the saddest time. I remember my mum crying all the time. I didn't really understand what was happening but I knew something big was up because my mum was so upset. We had to move to a council house in Haydock and she hated it. The kids there were really rough. I think it hit my mum hard. She saw me mixing with children who swore and got into trouble and she didn't want that for me. I was seen as the

1.2

posh girl and people thought they could pick on me because I didn't fit in, and I just took it. I had so many fights it was unreal. Girls used to gang up on me. I'd be going to the shop and they'd just grab me and pull my hair. I remember once being thrown into someone's garden. It was very frightening and very hard for my parents. When you see your child unhappy it gets you down. We had never been rich but we were comfortably off, then all of a sudden we had nothing, and that was difficult.

In the end they couldn't take it any more and we left the estate. We went to live with my sister and her husband until we were able to find another house. I loved being with my sister again. She had a baby and it was a nice experience for me. I remember sleeping on a camp bed in my mum and dad's room but I didn't mind. That was an odd time, especially for my mum. Having to stay with her daughter was a bit awful really. My dad never managed to build his business back up. We did buy another house but it wasn't anything spectacular and everything fell to pieces again because the work he was getting wasn't that regular.

I was also being bullied at school by fifth-formers. I was only in the first year so they were a lot bigger than me. I was a late developer and I used to get picked on for that. All the other girls were into boys and smoking and I never was. Also, I had something I wanted to do, and that made me different. I wanted to sing and be something. Even at that age I had a dream. By the time I was thirteen I had a record deal. I was signed up by a small label in Manchester called Jelly Street Records. Someone saw me singing and suggested I do a demo tape, so I did. The guy in the studio I used put me in touch with Kevin Kinsella, who owned Jelly Street, and he signed me up. I released a single called "One Kiss", which got in the charts, although I'm not sure how well it did. It wasn't bad for a young girl on a record label that was tiny.

Noel says: 'I always thought Kym was the strongest one in the band, but I don't any more. She's had quite a hard time in life generally and I think she has longed for this. I think *Popstars* was her last chance, and I think she just feels, Wow, because she made it, which is great. She's really cool.'

Garswood was a beautiful place to grow up.

On a camping holiday with my brother John – I can't remember who the other girl is!

I think the final straw at school came when I took a demo tape of songs into school and the girl who was the instigator of all the bullying took it and stamped on it. I flew at her and started hitting her – I know I shouldn't have but at that point something snapped inside me, and I'm glad it did because no one bothered me again. After that I wouldn't take anything from anybody. I was thirteen by then and I'd been bullied since I was ten. That's how long it took me to realize I should be sticking up for myself.

There's so much ignorance about bullying. Kids are killing themselves because they're scared to go to school. I used to say I was ill to avoid going in. My little boy, David, was being bullied when he first went into reception class. I had to go to his school so many times to sort it out.

When I was thirteen I went to the Elliot Clarke Stage School in Liverpool, which I enjoyed, but it was all dance and drama and I wanted to sing. We only did one day of singing a week, so it wasn't for me. I left when I was fifteen. I think that's when I started to worry about my weight. I was never a tiny girl, and I never will be because I'm big-framed. When I went to stage school there were girls who were a size six. I looked at myself and thought I must be fat because everyone else was stick thin. At that age you just feel different. I didn't do anything about it then but once I was sixteen I felt I wanted to lose weight and I started to make myself sick.

1.2

Myleene says: 'She's like the big sister I never had. I respect her so much. She's strong but she's also a very sensitive person. She's beautiful and very talented but she has all these insecurities. Actually, that's what makes her so lovely. She's a vulnerable person and that's what makes her appealing.'

My mum doesn't normally drink pints – I think that was for the camera.

Crying my eyes out!

Bulimia seemed so easy and I thought I'd be all right because I'd be able to control it. You never think it will get out of control. The first time I made myself sick I remember thinking, "I'm not going to do it again, it was a silly thing to do." But it's hard not to keep doing it. You think it's okay, you haven't died, you could do it just once more, but then it becomes second nature. I lost weight and went down to something ridiculous like just under seven stone when I should have been around eight and a half. I got to the stage where I was just eating and being sick naturally. Once you've been making yourself sick for a while your body picks up the habit and it becomes an automatic thing – it's like waking up in the morning.

At first I thought it was great. I was losing weight and that made me want to lose more, but nobody was telling me I looked good. Everyone was asking if I was all right. It was like, "You don't look well today, Kym. You're looking pale." I was tired and I couldn't concentrate. All I wanted to do was sleep because I had become quite weak. I would binge and then be sick and I had nothing in my system. I was doing it for about seven or eight months. I was underweight but I wasn't aware of it until I saw a picture of myself from a photo shoot and I was all bony. I just didn't look right. I went to my mum and told her what I'd been doing and she cried. It took me a while to recover and my mum used to watch me and get me to drink milk.

She still watches me. She doesn't have to, but she's determined I won't go down that road again. There was a story in the papers saying I was bulimic again, which was really out of order, and she freaked. I am not bulimic but I know that you can easily have a relapse if you're not strong enough mentally. I *am* strong enough and I've got three major reasons why I would never do it again, two of them being my children, because I love them too much. The other reason is that whatever I do influences children and I will not influence children to make themselves sick because it's wrong. Chocolate was always my weakness and it still is. But the difference now is I eat it and I enjoy it and I don't have a problem with that.

I was eighteen when I met Dave, the father of my children. We met in a pub and started going out. We'd only been together two months, which isn't a long time, when I found out I was pregnant with my first child, David, who's now five. The pregnancy was an accident. I was very naïve at the time. I'd been sick and didn't know that would stop the Pill from working. At the same time my dad had a heart attack, which was the scariest thing that has ever happened to me. I really thought I was going to lose him. I saw how my mum was and I just knew if anything had happened to him, God forbid, she would be a complete wreck. It was a terrible time. At that point I didn't have anything going on in my career so I concentrated on Dave and we spent a lot of time together.

My family was very supportive and I thought I'd be fine. Being pregnant was quite scary, but I'd seen my sister have three children, so I knew in a way what was going to happen to me. I knew I was going to get fat and that my legs would ache, basic things, but when it's happening to you it's a very different experience. People say it's the most brilliant thing in the world and it is, but it's also the most scary. I had a threatened miscarriage early on.

I started to bleed, for no reason, and I just had to rest. After that everything was fine until I got to around 33/34 weeks, when I went into spontaneous labour and was taken into hospital. They put me on a drip to stop the contractions and I had to have injections every twelve hours for two days. When they took me off the drip I was still having contractions, so they gave me the choice of either going back on a drip for another two weeks or having the baby. It was clear the baby was getting more

Danny says: 'You know where you stand with her, she'll tell you what she thinks. She's not as harsh or powerful as people portray her. Often behind powerfulness is a little bit of vulnerability somewhere. She definitely has a sweet, loving side to her. She's a mum and I think that is the ultimate thing – that's what sums her up. She's a positive role model.'

I got an early taste of filming when I was signed up by Jelly Street Records.

1.2

I was always a Daddy's girl. This one was taken at my son David's christening – I was christened on the same day.

distressed so I decided to just have it. I thought what will be will be. They told me there was a chance the baby might be blind or have something wrong with it but that nine times out of ten everything is fine. In the back of my mind I knew something might go wrong but I tried not to think about it.

I had David at 4.47 a.m. the following morning. My mum was there and my sister and Dave. My dad was in the room but he was behind a curtain because he didn't really think he should be there! David weighed 4 lb 4 oz and he had legs like little pieces of string. He was tiny. They put him in my arms and as I was holding him he turned blue and stopped breathing and the nurses had to rush him out. The nurse had her fingers down his throat to keep the airways open. It was terrifying. When they brought him back he was a nice pink colour and they put him straight in an incubator. I didn't see him again until the next day. I went home after three days but they kept him for two weeks and that was a nightmare, leaving him. I'd go in twice every day to feed him and give him his bath. By the time he came home he weighed 5 lb 2 oz.

Everything was all right for a while but Dave and I had a lot of problems, first of all because we didn't have a place to live. Dave's dad died when he was fifteen and his mum remarried and moved away, leaving Dave and his brother in their old house. I was staying there virtually all the time but because of the baby we had to find a place of our own. We bought somewhere cheap that needed a lot of work and for a while after the baby was born we stayed with my parents and tried to make the place liveable. Once we moved in, there was still a lot to be done and there was always work going on. Dave was quite old-fashioned and liked his tea on the table and thought the house should be clean and tidy. I tried, but with all the building going on it was difficult.

TIME CHECK

Kym's birthday – 13 June 1976 – saw The Wurzels at the top of the charts with Combine Harvester (Brand New Key).

We had lots of arguments and eventually things came to a head and we split up for about six months. I went back to my parents' but we were still seeing each other, trying to sort things out, and I got pregnant again. It was a bit of a shock. I couldn't remember us having any accidents but we must have. It had been very traumatic having David and some people would not have wanted another, but I don't think like that. They're worth it; I'd do it all over again. I believe in fate – there are things that are meant to be and if you fall pregnant it's for a reason.

I did have cravings when I was pregnant. With David it was chips and peas – I'd have that for my dinner every day from the chip shop down the road. I also craved cream eggs. With Emily it was ice cubes! I'd just have a pint glass filled with ice cubes and I'd crunch my way through them. I just liked the texture.

Dave and I got back together and I had Emily, who's now three. I went full term with Emily – she was 7 lb 8 oz. When she was twelve months old he and I were still fighting like cat and dog, and in front of the children, which wasn't good. We were supposed to get married but a few months before the wedding I left. It was a difficult decision to make because I had nothing and I had to think of the children's welfare. Emily was still too young to know what was going on but David was older and that was tough. But I knew I was doing the right thing for all of us.

I think the key thing was to make sure they didn't lose contact with their dad, so we came to an arrangement where he sees them three times a week. We did it properly. We didn't get on at all when we were together, but now we're apart there's no pressure. I love him because he's the father of my kids and he'll always be a big part of my life.'

With Emily on our way home after a holiday abroad.

My children are my world.

1.3

MYLEENE'S STORY

Suzanne says: 'She's very caring, she always puts everyone before herself. She has a wise business head and I admire that. She's very talented, musically, and she has an amazing voice. I really look up to her. She has a lot of qualities I'd like and she has huge respect for her family.'

'I grew up in Gorleston, in Norfolk. At the time it seemed like an average childhood but, looking back, it was quite extraordinary. My dad was away quite a lot because he was a diver and then a ship's captain, but when he was home it was for long, concentrated periods of time, which was even better. I just remember that every time he came home he brought all these presents from abroad. I remember music being played in the house all the time. Music was always there. My grandmother lived in Wales and I'd drive down with my dad and we'd make a pact. I could play two of my songs and he'd play two of his, so I'd have Kylie's "I Should Be So Lucky" and "Locomotion", and he'd have *Aida*. He introduced me to classical music and my mum encouraged me to play instruments. There's this story of how they were walking past a music shop and saw a tiny violin and my dad decided to buy it for me. I was two years old. I started violin and piano lessons when I was four.

I'm the eldest. My sister Jessie is two years younger and my brother Dan is two years younger than her but we always had a rule that we all respected each other. It was always drummed into us that we should never fight, we should always help each other, that no one had an advantage through age or whatever.

I was really lucky growing up in Gorleston because we were about three minutes from the beach, so I could hang out there with friends, and I could go strawberry picking

Some people have a paddling pool, me and my sister Jessie preferred a tin bath in the garden.

One of my earliest memories is playing with beer cans on the beach in the Bahamas.

because the forest was about ten minutes away, so it was wicked. I was always doing music and dancing lessons and I was such a girly girl when I was a kid – always in flowery, frilly dresses. My sister and I used to wear identical dresses and have our hair done the same when I was little. Then I went through my tomboy stage when you couldn't get me out of jeans. My mum and dad instilled a sense that family always comes first and, whatever, we would always stick together. That's really important to me. All of us in the band have strong families.

My mum's from a large family – there were seven children – and they were very close. Then, as they got older, there were jealousies and people moving away and it all just started to fracture. I know that was very painful for my mum. On my father's side there was favouritism. He was the youngest of three boys and they're no longer close. I didn't realize how much my mum and dad suffered, but basically I didn't grow up with any aunties or uncles. I've got hundreds of cousins but I don't see any of them. I used to see my grandmother in Wales but that was it really. I didn't grow up with any kind of extended family. I hear Danny talk about his nan, his aunts and his cousins but I never had any of that. And because my mum and dad have been hurt they practically built a wall around us and it's very hard for anyone else to penetrate that. They're so determined that we stay a close family unit.

As a result, I never had any serious fall-outs with my brother or sister, although I do remember once arguing with my sister when I was fourteen, and slamming the door on her. She made a huge fuss and said I'd hurt her eye. I didn't believe her but the next day she had the biggest black eye and I felt so bad. She looked like she'd been beaten up. I cried my eyes out. I didn't mean to hurt her.

When I was little I'd go away with my dad. I've been to most countries because of his job, so I've seen a mix of cultures. All my early photographs are of me diving with my dad. One of my earliest memories is playing with beer cans on the beach in The Bahamas! When you travel you get a sense of a bigger picture. We'd drive across Europe on holiday and I used to play the violin in the Wine Gardens in Vienna. I've had some amazing experiences.

Noel says: 'I don't think people have a true perception of her from *Popstars*. They think she's bossy and she's not. She knows what she wants and she'll always stand up for the band. She's very kind, very giving and exceptionally talented – so knowledgeable. I think she is underestimated.'

1.3

Mum and Dad probably thought I'd be pleased with my birthday cake, but I look a bit startled.

I developed a taste for pop at an early age.

I was very fortunate to have a really good education. My first two schools – St Mary's and Notre Dame – were Catholic schools, so when I went to secondary school it felt bizarre. They didn't say mass like I was used to, and all I'd ever known was being taught by nuns, so it seemed strange when I arrived at Cliff Park High. It was during that period, when I was about twelve, that I had my first kiss. His name was Rodney and we banged teeth! I was totally smitten with him because everyone fancied him and I was chuffed to bits he fancied me. We kissed at a disco. I was so embarrassed when our teeth clashed. You just know boys are going to tell all their friends. Then the next day we kissed again and, I'm not kidding – I had to spit into my cardigan! I just thought, "What is that all about?" But then when you find someone you really want to kiss you realize what the big deal is. Rodney was my boyfriend for a while, then I left that school and we swore eternal love for one another. Then I never heard from him again! I know where it all went sour. I bought him an Easter egg and he didn't get me one. I went out on my bike to get it and it cost £3.20! Sad, isn't it? I think we went out for about six weeks. True love!

I've got this way of putting things to the back of my mind, or even blocking things out, if I don't want to deal with them. I think I can still do that now and it's a crazy way to deal with things. If I can see a way out I'll sit down and talk it through. If it's really horrendous, I'll bury my head in the sand. I was bullied at school but I blocked it out. I was such a happy child, then I went to school and that's when I started to get picked on. Even at primary school kids used to take my lunch and kick my lunch box around. I was always being made fun of. I wanted to be in the school choir and the orchestra, and that wasn't a cool thing to do. I used to try to hide my violin and find different ways of making it look cool. In the end I got a strap and a square case and that looked cool. I was teased incessantly.

There was a boy who used to chase me and grab me – he was always doing things like spitting on my desk. One day when he was chasing me I ran smack into a door. I can just remember him saying, "I didn't do anything." The next thing I knew, I was in an ambulance with my head bleeding. Later, I woke up in hospital with my mum crying and me a right mess. I had a concussion and was off school for a week. I was truly knocked out. My mum and dad had words with his parents, and with the school, but he was never punished. When I got back to school, the headmistress called me in and made me say, "You're a bully, I'm not afraid of you," a hundred times. That was never going to work.

The bullying carried on into high school. I took some friends to the cinema on my thirteenth birthday. My dad had given me £50 to pay for everyone and buy drinks

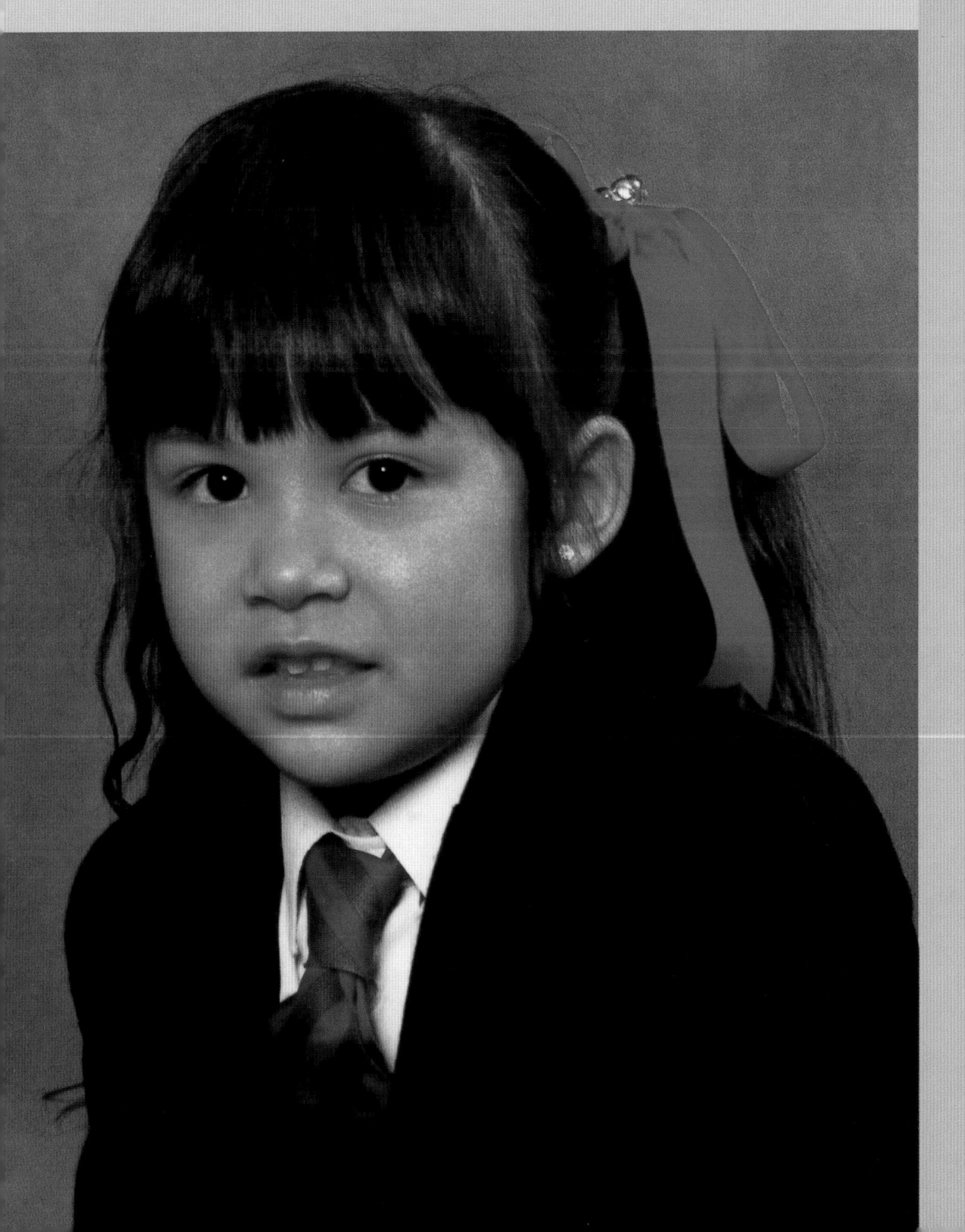

Danny says: 'She has very good leadership skills. She has a vast knowledge of different cultures because she got to see the world at a young age. She brings a lot to the group and is definitely into her family, her mum – aunty Bong, as we call her – and her dad, uncle Bing. She's so talented and very kind-hearted. She'll watch your back. And she's always good for a cuddle.'

I was always academic, but I hated Home Economics.

1.3

I was lucky growing up in Gorleston because we were about three minutes from the beach.

We're such a close family – that's really important.

and stuff. The people who bullied me at school followed us and sat behind us. I was too scared to turn round and say anything. All through the film popcorn was landing on my head, and they put chewing gum in my hair. My dad had to put surgical spirit on a comb to try and get the chewing gum out. In the end he had to cut it out. He was so angry.

One day these girls were waiting for me outside choir. They were eating grapes and spitting them at me. This girl had me up against the wall and she said, "I'm going to smack you." I said, "Go on then," because I didn't know what else to say. I could never have stood up to her – she was huge. They were all older than me, never my age. I'm not a fighter so I couldn't physically fight back and I couldn't talk to them because people like that don't want to talk.

I just used to try to get through things day to day. I didn't realize how much it affected me. At first I think I went into myself, then I went the other way and was really loud. I was just trying to find a way of coping. They were really traumatic times. Half of me was scared and half of me was ashamed. It's like, how uncool is it for your mum and dad to come to the school? I never considered myself a victim – I just accepted that there are all kinds of people out there and just got on with what I wanted to do – namely music.

I do think adults have a responsibility when there is bullying. There were teachers who were on the side of the bullies and there were teachers who chose to pick on certain kids. Even now I can't understand that. My drama teacher picked on me all the time and humiliated me in front of the class. I genuinely suffered at her hands. I remember at one of my school open evenings a teacher turned to my dad and said, "You've got to remember, Mr Klass, that when Myleene walks out of the school gates we're never going to hear from her again." He said, "You are so wrong," and we walked out. I don't know why a teacher would feel like that.

I never asked to be bullied. I thought it was maybe the way I looked or dressed or spoke. I am such a mixture – my mum's half Spanish, half Filipino, and my dad's half Austrian, half English, so that makes me a quarter of everything. Then I come out with this English accent and that just confuses people even more. Then there's the name – Myleene Angela Klass – crossing everything. I also felt ugly all the time. I used to hide behind my glasses. Before I even washed my face in the morning I'd get my glasses on. I never let anyone see me without my glasses. I hated swimming because it meant the glasses had to come off. I just felt ugly because no one looked like me and, at the time, I just wanted to look like everyone else. I was always trying to reinvent myself with my looks. That fitting-in thing is so important for a child, but the more I tried, the worse it got, really.

Of course, now it would be a problem if I looked like everyone else, because I wouldn't be where I am. I remember going up for a part in *Les Misérables* and looking at the other girls and thinking I just didn't look like your typical wench who's going to serve you a pint. I thought, "What am I doing here?" Now that's my saving grace because I've got a different look and people notice that.

say

Kym says: 'She thinks everything through, she's very organized, although sometimes she does forget things. She's very supportive. If you have a problem, you know she'll help you through it.'

I can't quite decide whether to throw this giant snowball.

1.3

I was a very girly girl – my sister and I always wore identical dresses

I'm not sure how I feel now, looking back. I just look at what I've achieved and that's my power. Now I feel strong and able to stand up for myself. I've had to learn how to fight – not physically but verbally. I don't feel I was a victim, because the problem was theirs, not mine. Besides, there are people who have had so much more to deal with in their lives.

When I was older, I put my mum and dad through hell. Especially when I got my first boyfriend. I'd had boyfriends before but he was the first cool one. None of the guys would date me because I wasn't cool. I knew my dad didn't approve of him so I used to sneak out. I was crazy. I think I just went to excess because I felt I had something to prove to everybody and all I ended up doing was hurting my mum and dad and myself. It all stopped one day when I came home in the early hours and I was climbing over the car to get through the garage and in the back door. I was in this long dress from the night before and suddenly I felt so cheap and nasty. I thought, "What am I trying to do?"

I feel very lucky to come from such mixed cultures. As a child you don't really perceive it as anything out of the ordinary, but now I'm older, I can see what a broad perspective it's given me. Plus, with all the other mixtures in our band, it's not only a sign of the times, but a walking Benetton ad! I think all of us in the band went through that sense of being the odd one out. You just have to find your niche, and what's happened with Hear'say is that five like-minded people have come together. It's like fitting five pieces of a jigsaw together.

TIME CHECK

On Myleene's birthday – 6 April 1978 – Kate Bush topped the charts with Wuthering Heights

When I was fourteen I started music school and was commuting at weekends to the Guildhall School of Music. That was an experience because I met like-minded people and, travelling to London on my own, I grew up. I suddenly found some confidence and everything became clearer. My parents said the change in me was phenomenal. I walked into a room of thirty kids, and I'm not saying anyone looked odd, it's just that you could see their individuality. Suddenly I was able to sit and have amazing conversations with people who were in tune with me. I used to go to their parties and they'd sit round and play the piano like I did. I remember one party and there was a game where everyone had to do four bars improvisation on the piano and no one could break the chain and I was like, *yes-s-s*! It was just amazing to find people on my wavelength.

There was only one time I remember really struggling with my work and that was when I was in the middle of my GCSEs. I was taking my Grade 7 violin and piano at the same time – usually you'd only do one in a year – and I remember waking up crying thinking I'd missed my science exam. How sad is that! I just had to try my best at everything, otherwise I'd kick myself afterwards. It all got a bit much at that point. My problem was that I could have gone in lots of different directions. I thought my head would explode. I wanted to do pop but I knew that wasn't realistic. I was also teaching piano and singing at the time and it was great to see people come out of their shell and improve. My dad once said he'd help me set up a music school and maybe eventually I'd like to do that, but I had to do something for me first.

As well as all my extra-curricular work, I loved the academic side of things – especially English Literature and astronomy. The only subject I hated with a passion was Home Economics, I switched off in those lessons. I was never really disruptive, but I did tend to talk a lot. I loved A levels because they were the subjects I chose to specialize in. I did English – which really opened my eyes to reading – and theatre and music. I did the history of music anthology and music dictation and was able to write down a piece after listening to it once. I loved it. I didn't have a strict upbringing. My parents just always encouraged me to do my best.

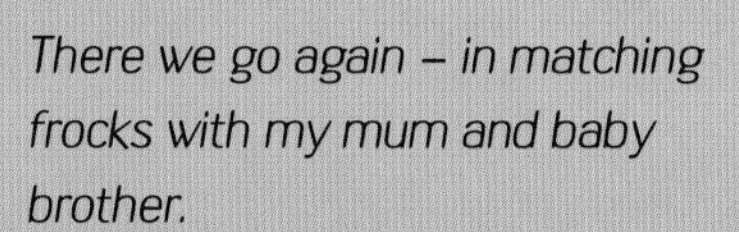

I was sixteen when I went for my first audition at the Guildhall, but I was so nervous, I was useless. I got the job but my dad thought I was going to faint. I looked like a

There we go again – in matching frocks with my mum and baby brother.

1.3

I used to hide behind my glasses.

beetroot and I was close to hyperventilating. He asked me afterwards if I was sure that's what I wanted to do and I wondered if I was really going to be able to get through it. I thought, "Is this going to happen every time I walk on stage?" But it's a mind-over-matter thing and I just don't get nervous now. I get a kick out of excitement. This is my job and I've learned to enjoy it rather than fear it.

I didn't do a degree – I went straight to the Royal Academy of Music to do a postgraduate course instead. My singing teacher there, Mary Hammond, asked me if I knew what the school expected of me. I'd never even thought about it. She told me she was going to stop me from hiding behind make-up, because at that stage I wore loads of it. I really used to pile it on and I did hide behind it. I used to paint my face and I looked like a clown. She wanted to get me out of that and I remember being petrified at the thought of people seeing me without make-up. When I left college I still couldn't get out of wearing make-up, but *Popstars* did it. I was living in the house, getting up in the morning with this new family, and they saw me at my worst and at my best. That gave me so much confidence, and then having success made me realize I could do the job. Now I feel I could go anywhere in my jeans and no make-up because it's more about what I've done and what I have to say than how I look. That's been a massive lesson. I don't feel I need to hide any more and that's so liberating. I can be myself and feel confident in my work and I'm really happy. I'd never call myself pretty but I'm more than happy to face people now. The other morning we had an early start and I arrived at this TV studio in my pyjamas and with no make-up. I actually hate wearing make-up now because we have to wear so much. But it took *Popstars* to make me feel like this.

I remember being really worried during the last couple of weeks of my postgraduate course. That's when you have all the auditions and everyone talks about what they're going to be doing. I hadn't heard anything, then a few days before I left college I heard I had a place in *Miss Saigon* and also in *Jesus Christ Superstar*, so I had to make a choice. It was the best feeling in the world. I chose *Miss Saigon* because it was the West End and I'd be doing both the tenth anniversary show and the final show. Plus, it was in Covent Garden so I could go shopping! I had an amazing time but it was really hard work. Sometimes I didn't know what day it was. I had to work really hard, prove myself all the time. I remember once they brought in this "swing" – that's what they call people who can cover anyone's part – and she was singing her heart out on stage but they didn't light her. For some reason it made me laugh. I just corpsed. Laughing on stage is like laughing in church – it's not allowed. I could not stop and it was a really sad scene. Everyone else was crying and I was killing myself laughing. Another time the sequins on my tights locked together and I ended up waddling off stage like a penguin!

After *Miss Saigon* I worked with Cliff Richard for two months. He was amazing, so nice. Then I went straight off to tour with Michael Crawford and I sang backing vocals for k.d. lang on *Parkinson*. Auditioning is not an easy process – you have to learn to be strong and take rejection, but also to believe in yourself enough to turn any criticism into a positive situation. You learn to create opportunities for yourself instead of waiting for things to come to you.'

You don't get a sense of how big the pyramids are from this picture – they are huge!

1.4 NOEL'S STORY

Danny says: 'Noel is probably a lot smarter than people realize. Everyone says he's funny, makes you laugh, good impressionist, but he's also really smart. He's well travelled. When we went to Spain recently he was speaking fluent Spanish. I'd never seen that side of him before. He's very into his family. His mum is the be all and end all, which is how it should be. He's definitely a Welsh boy and he's my best mate. He's just really cool. He's the brother I never had.'

This was taken when I was one and hadn't discovered baseball caps.

Myleene says: 'He's such a compassionate person. He has the biggest heart and his family comes first. Everyone always paints Noel as the joker but he's also very clever. His appreciation of music is quite overwhelming. His head is always spinning with ideas. He's such a funny character – you can be talking to him and think he's ignoring you but it's just he's miles away – it drives Danny mad!'

'We moved a lot when I was a kid, lived in lots of different areas around Cardiff. I had a good childhood and I remember music was always a big part of it. I used to go and stay with my *meme* (my nan) every Friday night. She is a classically trained cellist and she teaches piano and violin, so she had a piano in the house. My grandmother is French and you can't find a more French person – just the way she speaks, her manners, her cooking. She was strict with me and would go on at me to practise. She had a lot of influence on my music. I'd have choir practice on a Saturday morning. I was in a choir called the Scallywags. It was all kids and I joined when I was about six. I had piano lessons as well, and I remember always being told off for not practising. Then I started singing lessons when I got a bit older. I used to do eisteddfods and I'd win all the time. I was always coming home with the trophy and medals for singing. My musical background is really useful. To know how things are supposed to sound — I really appreciate that. I appreciate classical musicians and singers as much as I appreciate pop. I think my grandmother always thought I'd do something classical but now she sees me on *Top of the Pops*. She has a poster of me and Danny in the dining room, which I find so peculiar because with pop music she always used to be, "Turn that racket off!"

My relationship with my mum is really close.

I was only two weeks old when this was taken.

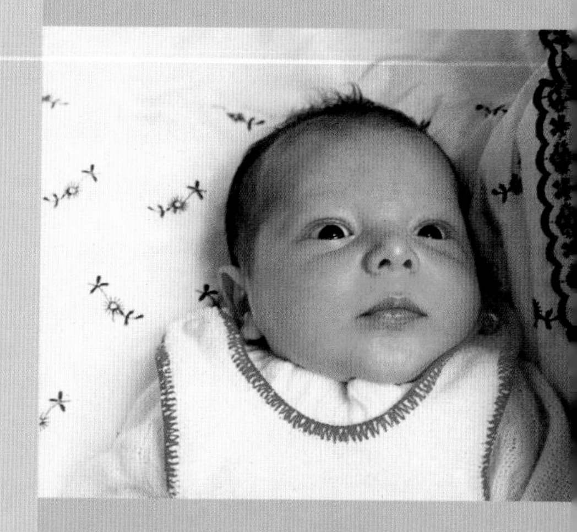

1.4

Bath time was play time – but these days I'd rather have a shower.

My mum and dad split up when I was six and I lost touch with my dad. Then my mum met Colin, my step-dad. They got married when I was nine or ten, so I view him as my dad. He and my mum split when I was sixteen and doing my GCSEs. It was an amicable split, but I remember I hated seeing my mum upset because I'd seen her upset so much. Even now I resent him for that, but we all make mistakes – it's part of life. My relationship with my mum got really close at that point. It always had been, but it became more so. I think I started to grow up a bit. I was the man of the house and I was happy with that. Colin brought me up and supported me through school and I'm still in touch with him now, but my mum is the constant person in my life. It would be hard to pick up my old relationship with him now – I'm a different person. From sixteen to twenty-one is such a life-changing time.

My mum worked nights at the hospital when I was at school. We'd pick her up in the morning before I went to school, then she'd go to bed during the day and pick me up from school. We'd spend the evening with her until she went off to work again at the end of the day, by which time I had to go to bed anyway.

I hated school. I don't remember much about primary school but I won a scholarship to go to a private choir school, St John's College, in Cardiff. I was there from the age of nine to around thirteen, then I left to go back to a normal secondary school. St John's was good because I got massive musical experience from a young age without even thinking about it.

Kym says: 'You know when he's down because he goes very quiet – usually all it takes is a trip to Cardiff to sort him out.
He's very funny, very talented.
I love him.'

I hated school – not that you'd guess it from this picture.

1.4

TIME CHECK

On 28 July 1980, Odessey was at Number One with Use It Up and Wear it Out, and Noel was born.

I caught these without any help – well, maybe just a little.

Celebrating my sixth birthday.

I had my first girlfriend at St John's. Her name was Kimberley and I went out with her for a bit, sent her love letters in class, and we used to meet in the playground for a snog. I must have been about twelve. It didn't last very long. In my early teens I used to snog everyone, I was really bad! Even so, I felt like St John's wasn't my world. I didn't enjoy it and I think that was partly because of money. The friends I had were all from really wealthy families and I was only there because I'd won a scholarship and my nan helped out with the fees. There were always these school trips to stupid places. Most schools go to the local zoo, but they'd go to Austria skiing, and it isn't easy to raise that kind of money.

So I went back to Mary Immaculate High School. I remember I used to get grief there from all the rugby lads because I hated PE and games. I stuck with my music and I'd sing in every concert. That was my thing and I loved it, which wasn't the best thing perhaps when you're a teenage boy. It's like being into dance or something – it's just not what most teenage boys do. Although I had some good friends there and some good teachers, I couldn't wait for the day I left. I used to get told off all the time for not doing my homework. The teachers knew I could do it, so they'd be on my back all the time. I was just lazy but I was still able to pull my exams out of

I was aware that we struggled, but on the whole I had a very happy childhood.

Suzanne says: 'I feel like I'm really close to Noel at the moment. We're a similar age and from a similar family background. He's a very clever lad and he's someone I can really talk to and tell exactly how I feel. I think we've both had the same bad press and we talk all the time. He is such a caring lad. Noel knows when to leave people alone but he also knows when to cheer you up. The number of times he has made me laugh when it was the last thing I felt like doing. I look up to him and Danny as big brothers.'

the bag. I got eight GCSEs, which wasn't bad. But there was one teacher, Miss Gillings, who used to tell me to keep singing and that I'd do really well with it one day.

When I went to sixth form college it was like a breath of fresh air because I wasn't the only person in the school who liked music any more. I chose theatre studies, media studies and music as my options and suddenly I was with people who were into exactly the same things as me. I felt a huge change in me, confidence-wise — it was like finding yourself at sixteen. I started to get to grips with what I really wanted to do, which was perform, but because it was such a great experience I didn't concentrate on my work as much as I should have. I was just enjoying it. My sixth form friends are still some of my closest. I had a really good teacher there, Mr Tunley, who taught us to keep our feet on the ground. I take that with me everywhere now. He was an inspiration and I really admired him.

I used to get name-called at school, and there was a bit of bullying, but I just thought that's what everyone got. It didn't affect me. It depends how big a deal you make of it. I could brush it off and walk away. I think I always knew I was going to do something good later on and all those people who took the mick are still working in the local supermarket, still doing the same things, hanging round with the same people. They haven't moved on and I have. It wasn't like I had a grand plan or anything, but I never felt I'd be able to hold down a nine-to-five job.

I worked at British Gas for a few months and I hated it. I much preferred working in a restaurant where your shifts changed on a weekly basis. When I left British Gas I went to Ibiza and did a season working as a puppeteer, then came back and worked in a restaurant for a bit. In Ibiza I was just waiting for something to come along that had something to do with performance – something that wasn't regimented. I didn't have a clue what it was going to be about until I got there. My first impressions were horrible. The season doesn't open until the beginning of May and we arrived in mid-April. There was nothing there, nobody. They gave us a video of the show and left us to it. By the end of the week we knew it by heart.

The season was brilliant though. I was staying in a really nice apartment on the top floor of a block and it had a massive balcony. It was lovely – you could see the sea from the balcony. I met loads of different people. The work was just performing the show for a couple of hours every night. Apart from that we had free time. It was like being on holiday. The only time I got homesick was mid-season. Everyone does at that point because you can't see the end of it, but it wasn't like I was at the other end of the earth. I was only a couple of hours away on a plane, so it was fine. I came back when the season finished at the end of October. Then I tripped and dislocated my knee and didn't work for a couple of months. It went a few times again afterwards, just doing things like getting on the bus or walking down the stairs. I'm in physio now so it should be fine.

I think all the things I did when I left college made me realize I wanted to try for something more. I suppose it's in your make-up from an early age, the desire to

With my nan and cousins – my mum and step-dad Colin are peering through the curtains behind us.

1.4

I finally started to get to grips with what I really wanted to do – which was perform.

My mum treasured me.

escape from it all or a willingness to just fit in, and I don't think I've ever been prepared to do that. I think I must get it from my mum. Seeing her struggle and always come out the other side smiling, even if she didn't feel it inside – that was amazing. Sometimes I think it's all about karma; we've had such a rough time of it that something has to come right somewhere. My little brother was a cot death victim and my baby sister died from a brain tumour when she was just nine days old. There has been a lot of tragedy but people don't see that. They see you on *Popstars* and just think you're the funny one or whatever, but they don't actually appreciate what's gone on in your life. I was aware that we struggled when I was little and looking back I can remember bad times, but on the whole there were very good times as well and I had a very happy childhood. My mum absolutely treasured me because I was the only one. I never felt I wanted for anything and my mum would go without, to get me the latest bike, or whatever. I don't know how she managed it, but you just do, don't you? If you're a survivor you survive. We've always had a cast-iron relationship. We do argue, like any mother and son, but the foundation is strong.

When I was younger I never gave her any cause for concern; I wasn't off nicking cars or anything. I could have hung round with the wrong crowd but I didn't — I didn't want to get stuck.'

I'm a real sun worshipper.

With my mum and Kerry – one of my closest friends. We went to Ibiza to do the puppet show together.

1.5 SUZANNE'S STORY

Kym says: 'I feel very protective towards Suzy. I just want to be there for her. She is a very funny girl, comes out with silly little things that make you laugh. She can be hilarious.'

'When I was little we lived in a big old Victorian house in Bury. From about the age of three I remember dancing in the front room and thinking I wanted to be in Hollywood. My dad, Vinnie, is a cameraman and so a lot of my childhood is on film. I was always performing for the camera.

I was two when I started ballet. My brother Paul had started dancing classes so I went with him. When I was three I changed dance schools and did everything – ballet, tap, modern, a bit of jazz and street dancing. I was never into ballet. I was always the fat kid, which got me down a lot. I've always been up and down with my weight and I think that's why I'm insecure about it. I used to stand there in ballet with all these twig-thin ballerinas. I remember my dance teacher saying, "You could do many things, but you'll never be a ballerina."

Then I went into acting and did my first show, *Annie*, when I was five. That was my first audition and I can remember being in tears when I came out. I did a song and

Me, my mum and brother – I was only about three months old when this was taken.

We can't wait to eat the cake – me and my friends at my seventh birthday party.

(below) In the garden with my brother.

Danny says: 'She's very funny and she's cute but there's more to her than that. She's the youngest but she's as old as the rest of us in her head. She's strong but she sometimes has low confidence, although she's much better now than she used to be. She's very caring and thoughtful – a good mate.'

dance and everyone laughed. I thought they were laughing at me and I got really upset. When I got the part I was really confused! Then I did *The Sound of Music*, then *Annie* again. I joined an amateur dramatics society and every year we did a production. I started to get more serious about acting. I did a West End production of *Showboat* when I was nine, then I landed a TV role in the BBC series *Elidor*.

I was twelve years old and I thought it was my big break. I really thought I was made for life. Later, I discovered it's not as easy as that and I went on to do more auditions, and got turned down a fair bit. I remember feeling so grown up on *Elidor* because I was socializing with older people. I also met my first boyfriend, Damien. He was a couple of years older than me and he was playing the part of my brother. It was all very innocent. We used to hold hands in secret. I had my first kiss with Damien. We were filming in Wales and by the end of the first week he got the courage up to kiss me. There were a load of chalets everyone stayed in and we kissed behind them. At the time I thought he knew what he was doing but he had no idea! It felt really weird afterwards, like I'd done something really naughty.

I did some radio productions and some commercials here and there, then when I was fifteen I decided I wanted to sing. I always did a lot of song and dance festivals and I used to win trophies all the time. There are lots of trophies with my name on

1.5

Catch! I loved sport when I was at school.

Myleene says: 'She has got the kindest heart. We talk and talk and she is always there for me. She is such a giving person, she has nothing but good things to say about people. I have such a lot of respect for her. I think if anyone hurt Suzy I'd smack them!'

them, but people might not realize because not everyone knows my name is actually Crowshaw, not Shaw.

I always remember school being a chore. Everyone says school days are the best, but they're not. School was difficult, not because I couldn't do the academic work – I was fine with that. It was more that people didn't understand why I did the performing. It was quite difficult and teachers would question why I wanted time off for auditions. I used to love PE, art, English, drama and music, but hated maths and science. RE was okay because we had a really cool Irish teacher. In all my reports the teachers would say, "She's a really clever girl but she could do better." It was because I didn't want to be there – I wanted to be rich and famous. I still managed to get nine GCSEs, even though I felt a bit like a square peg in a round hole at school.

Although I had friends, I wasn't interested in being with them, which sounds horrible, but they looked at life in a totally different way. I had so many ambitions that no one thought a girl from Bury was capable of achieving. I got teased a lot. When I did *Elidor* one kid came up and told me I was rubbish. That really upset me. There were some horrible comments. The same happened to my brother. He gave up dancing to fit in with his friends, whereas I walked away from my friends to be a performer. I just wanted a lot more for myself. I've no idea where that came from. It wasn't because I was confident about how good I was. It was just because I wanted it so much. I wasn't the best singer or dancer or actress but I wanted it badly. No matter how many knocks or rejections I got, I thought, "Never mind – chin up, carry on."

I got into music at my primary school, St Mary's, in Radcliffe. I learned to play the recorder and the violin. Then when I got to secondary school, St Gabriel's in Bury, I started to learn the saxophone and I loved it. I stopped after two years because my mum, Janet, and my dad were already paying for dancing and singing lessons and the sax was a bit too much on top of all that. When I think about it they must have paid out thousands for me on classes, dance shows and stuff. They even had to get a tutor in for me because I was missing so much school. They deserve a lot of credit for getting me where I am now. It was a strain for them to provide ballet shoes, leotards, dance lessons, singing lessons. Not a lot of kids got those opportunities because their parents couldn't afford it, and I'm really grateful. If I ever make my millions I'll look after them. They just worked constantly to pay for everything.

It was pretty much a happy childhood but they weren't all good times. My mum and dad split when I was fourteen and I know it sounds strange but I was glad, because for as long as I could remember they'd argued and it was difficult. They just weren't

If I dig deep enough, perhaps I'll get to Australia.

All dressed up for my first Holy Communion.

I started ballet when I was two.

right for each other. I know most kids hate their parents going through a split, but I didn't feel like that. I lived with my mum and my brother lived with my dad, but it wasn't a terrible time or anything. Now my mum's remarried and my dad's getting married at the end of the year, so they're both really happy and it's much better that way. It can be difficult now for them to be in the same room. Actually, *they* can be in the same room, but *I* feel awkward.

After they split and I stayed with my mum, she started seeing Ference – they're married now – and I found that difficult. I was sixteen and going through a stage of feeling insecure with friends and school and it was like, "This man has ruined my life." I couldn't get on with him, so for a while I went to live with my dad.

I made my feelings known to my mum and to Ference, I totally told him where to go. I was so horrible to him but now it's fine. I just came to realize that my mum wants her happiness, but at the time it felt like I'd suddenly lost her and it scared me. I'd have felt like that about any man in her life. I think he loved her too much to be bothered by me, but I was very stroppy.

I started going to auditions by myself, getting on the train to London on my own. Then I started going out with a lad and lost interest in auditions. I felt I wasn't getting anywhere, so what was the point? The one thing I really missed was the old house. I'd always had the small bedroom and my brother had the big one because he was older, but then we swapped. I was doing my girly stuff, I had more clothes and needed more space. Suddenly we had to move away and into a little granny flat in Bolton, which was gutting. I cried about it.

I didn't do A levels, but went to Oldham College for a BTEC in Performing Arts. That's when I grew up fast. I joined The Right Stuff, an Abba tribute band, and was suddenly surrounded by older people. Joining the band was a turning point. That's when I met Andrew, my boyfriend. I auditioned in his front room. I was so confident as I stood there and sang Alannis Morissette's "Ironic". He told me right away I'd got the job.

My mum always says I suddenly shot into adulthood overnight. I learned a lot about how to deal with people. I used to organize song lists, speak to agents, try and get

I always remember school as being a chore.

TIME CHECK

Adam and the Ants topped the charts with Prince Charming on 29 September 1981 – Suzanne's birthday.

more bookings for us. Andrew dealt with all the equipment and sorted out the backing tracks. In the end it was a partnership and I think it was really good for me.

Noel says: 'I think she's a beautiful person. I always thought she was strong but she has insecurities like the rest of us. I feel like we're in the same boat because we're around the same age and her family is far away, so it's hard for her to keep in touch. The more she sings the stronger she gets and she is shining at the moment. She has a fantastic voice and the personality to carry the whole pop star thing off.'

When I joined The Right Stuff I wasn't a pop singer. I was more musical theatre, and without that experience I don't think I'd be in Hear'say. All along I'd been into acting, then I realized I wanted to do pop and I became really determined. I took to it straight away, although I was so enthusiastic at my first gig that I jumped off the stage and into the audience. I was trying to get people up dancing, but I picked on the wrong person – this woman turned round and told me where to get off. It was a while before I tried that again! I had a lot of confidence at that point, I was singing well, and doing well at college. I did some sax pieces on stage and I was taking the lead on a lot of songs. I was really proud of myself. I ended up doing all the talking on stage. I'd tell really sad jokes, really cheesy stuff, but the audience loved it. They'd shout stuff at me and I'd be, "Whose microphone's louder, love, yours or mine?" I loved it. We travelled a fair bit as well, and played in Saudi Arabia and Bahrain. That was a huge experience for me.

I was going out with Paul when I first joined The Right Stuff. We had met at school and were together two and a half years, but it got to the point where we weren't really seeing each other. I was off during the day when he was busy and he was off at night when I was working. I split up with Paul, and Andrew was coming to the end of his relationship, so Andrew and I got together. For a while we were both friendly with our ex-partners, but both of them have sold stories about us. I knew Andrew's ex-girlfriend would but I thought Paul wouldn't. That shocked me. Andrew was a lot older and wiser than anyone I'd met before – he's sixteen years older than me. He had ambitions, like me, and he was just so kind and nice to me; he complimented me all the time and we're on the same wavelength. We've never been dead serious, but we're there for each other, we always have been.

Rollerskating limbo dancing!

With my co-star from an amateur production of The Boyfriend.

It was during this time that I started having panic attacks. When I had my first one I thought I was going to die. I didn't know what was happening to me. It was like I couldn't breathe and I was faint. I went into my brother's bedroom and asked him to take me to the hospital. He took me to my mum's and she managed to calm me down. She's a community psychiatric nurse and she deals with panic attacks all the time. She knew what was happening to me. Thankfully, they're a thing of the past. I haven't had anything like that for a long time.

We were so busy with the band that I left college without completing my diploma. My mum said I'd regret it, but I don't. *Popstars* was my first audition for a band. I can remember overhearing Nicki Chapman at the auditions saying, "You have to be able to get up in the morning and look in the mirror and believe you can be a pop star." I thought, "I can do that!" I was overly confident at first at the auditions but then my confidence deteriorated. I had so many insecurities – I always have.

One thing I wish is that my granddad had lived to see me have some success. I was really close to him but he died in February last year. That was hard because it was the first time I'd lost someone close to me. He had skin cancer and, despite radiotherapy, he just got more poorly. Then he got lung cancer and became really ill. The Christmas before he died I'd been working and I hadn't seen much of him, although I'd spoken to him. Then I came home and that's when I saw him. I've never been so shocked in all my life. He used to be a big guy and he'd turned into a frail old man. He had just deteriorated. By the end of February he didn't really know who we were. My nan was distraught and it was horrible seeing him in that state. I was really strong at the time. Even though I was upset I didn't shed any tears. It's only now it's really hurting and I've cried. I know if he was still around he would be my number one fan.'

POPSTARS IN THE MAKING

2

Kym: 'I knew inside I could make a decent life for my children and have my dream if the right thing came along. *Popstars* was the break I needed.'

32

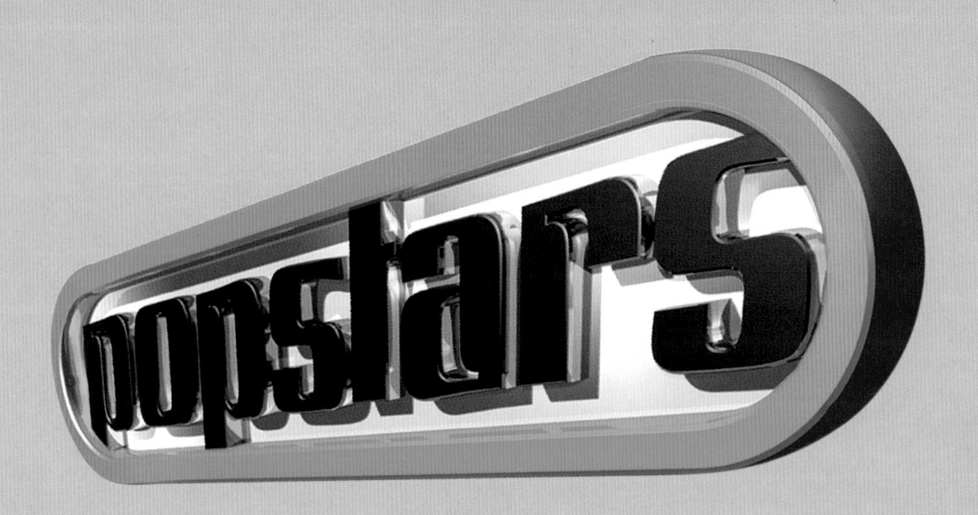

Nigel casts a professional eye over the contestants.

Danny: 'I didn't think I had a good voice. Then I got up on holiday – I was a bit drunk – and I sang karaoke, and people told me I could sing. It wasn't until I came home and I started singing a bit and got some offers of work that I thought, "This is good." At first I started with bands so there were four other people on the stage and it didn't feel like it was just me, then I started singing with backing tracks in local pubs. There was a demand for what I was doing and I found that amazing. At one stage I was singing on Friday and Saturday nights and doing two gigs on Sunday.

'I decided to have a year out after doing my childcare diploma and I went to a few auditions and found I was getting down to the last few. I'd be looking round the room and seeing all these people who'd been to stage school warming up, and I didn't even know what to do, and yet I was getting close.

'I decided to audition for Butlin's to be a redcoat and I got what they call principal gold, which meant I would be in a big show right away. When I went for my training people were saying I was so lucky to start at that level, but I hadn't realized. I went to Butlin's at Bognor Regis for training and I just didn't like it. I left after two days. Everyone was jumping around all the time. It was all very false and I couldn't settle, so I left. It's that thing about stability and things not feeling right. I knew I wouldn't feel comfortable in that environment. Maybe I just wasn't ready to leave home. It was the best decision I made. If I'd stayed maybe I wouldn't have done the *Popstars* audition. Just before *Popstars* I was still singing in pubs and working as a cleaner. I wasn't really fussed about going to the audition because I'd seen the advert in *The Stage* and rang the number for information and it was the most cheesy thing I've ever heard. 'Hi, welcome to *Popstars*!' It really was bad, so tacky. But then life's all about creating opportunities and I thought I should go because something else might come of it.'

Myleene: 'I didn't realize how big *Popstars* was going to be and I genuinely treated it just like any other job. The day I went for my audition at LWT in London I was working as a singer on the Lily Savage show in the studio next door. When I saw the cameras I knew I wanted to stay away from them because I could see they were trying to pick out characters. I knew if I didn't get into the band it would be, "Here's Myleene – she left her last job just hours before the auditions, she plays this instrument and that." And I felt it would have been very difficult to work afterwards.

'Now, looking back, people say I'd have been mad to miss *Popstars* but at the time I didn't know what was going to happen. I didn't know if I'd get it, I didn't know if I'd be paid. At the time I was due to go on tour as a singer with Robbie Williams and that was a proper job, so I had to decide. That was three months' work, which is a lifetime in performer land. It was the biggest gamble ever but it paid off. With hindsight, it's easy to see it was the right thing to do, but at the time no one knew if the show would fall on its face. You'd have been forever known as someone who didn't make it on *Popstars*. So I had doubts. Was this going to be one of those annoying fly-on-the-wall documentaries? I couldn't get a clear perspective on what was going on. I was used to normal auditions where if you didn't get it you walked out. Here you had Nigel and the drum roll – are you going to get it or not? Will you last another day? The stress! Everyone was looking ill. Looking back, I wonder how we did get through. I see my friends going for auditions all the time and I realize there aren't many jobs like this out there. I'm living proof the dream does come true.'

Kym: 'Before *Popstars*, I was living in a rented house with my children, David and Emily, finding it difficult to pay the bills. It was very hard to make ends meet. I was frustrated because I wanted to sing but I knew I couldn't do the clubs because I'd

Kym and Suzanne get to grips with a new routine.

have to give up my benefits and I knew I wouldn't earn enough to be able to do that. I'd given up hope of fulfilling the dream I had. I'd given up on singing. I always said if I didn't make it by the time I was twenty-five that would be it. I just thought the dream I had wasn't meant to be and that I had to concentrate on being a mum and trying to do the best for my children. There were days I felt I was banging my head against a brick wall because no matter what I did their lives didn't seem to get any better, and it used to break my heart.

'I knew inside that I could make a decent life for my children *and* have my dream if the right thing came along. *Popstars* was the break I needed.'

Noel: 'I remember getting to the auditions in London and thinking, "What am I meant to be?" I do remember deciding that I was going to be myself and thinking I can't get shot down for that. The whole workshop experience in London was designed for maximum TV impact, to bring out extremes in emotion. You can see that throughout the series, looking back. I don't think I was really aware of it until we watched the

Myleene studies some lyrics.

Noel takes a moment to watch the competition.

Kym and Myleene give their all.

episode of the five of us moving into the house and we saw the kind of things they'd focused on. We came to realize the power of editing and we started to be careful about what we were saying because we didn't want to give them ammunition to turn one of us into the big bad wolf. I think they were really gutted that we didn't all argue in front of the cameras. If we did have a discussion we'd wait until doors were closed, cameras were off, and people were asleep. That was our way of keeping our sanity because if you give everything to the camera there's nothing left for yourself.'

Danny: 'I knew as soon as we moved into the house that we were all going to get on, but I still wasn't sure whether it was going to work. I think the production team – the crews and the directors – worked hard, and I think they helped make Hear'say.'

Noel: 'I remember wondering if I was making the right decision because I was giving up my life for something that might not work. I was very uncertain about what the future might hold. No one knew how it was going to go. I don't think I remember a point where I thought, "Yeah, this is okay" – it just evolved. We went from being strangers to the way we are now, all very close and getting on.

TIME CHECK
Popstars *audition song* Bridge over Troubled Water *was a hit for Simon and Garfunkel in 1970.*

2.0

'I think one of my biggest worries has always been, "How long is this going to last and what's going to happen when it ends?" I do think about that but then I stop because there's no answer. It does worry me that the next big thing is going to come along and totally obliterate us. I know it's a fickle industry but I don't want people to abandon us. I know we can't control that, but we've given up everything for this and if it goes really soon all we'll have is a mad year of memories, which is quite scary.'

Suzanne: 'We genuinely didn't know how big *Popstars* was going to be. I can remember being in the house, living in secret, and thinking, "Is anyone going to care about us? Is anyone going to watch this show?" We just didn't know. Then all this stuff started appearing in the papers and we were just amazed. We always talk about being in the *Popstars* bubble and that's how it was. What was happening in the world outside was much bigger than we appreciated.'

Danny: 'I did a lot of crying at the auditions and that's not me at all. I don't know why it happened. I was aware of the fact it was a TV show and that a lot of people would see

TIME CHECK

While Suzanne auditioned for her place in the band, her favourite song, Dancing in the Moonlight by Toploader was No. 11 in the charts.

A difficult choice!

A rare moment of relaxation for Suzanne.

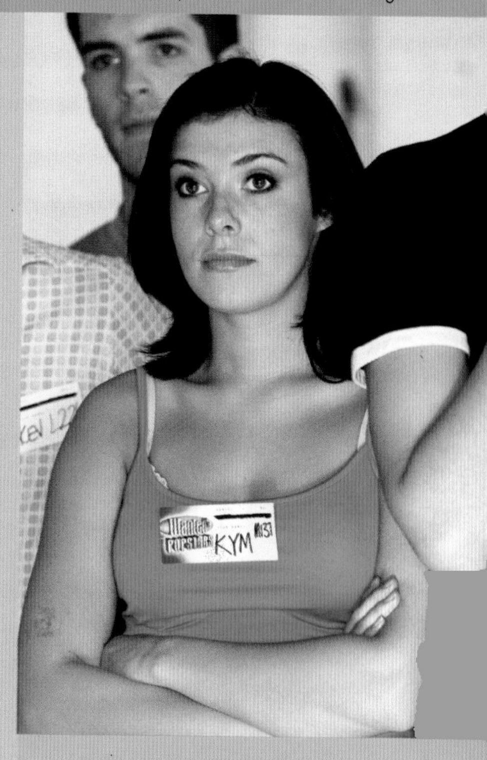

The tension mounts for Kym.

it, although I didn't appreciate how many. I wondered how I would be portrayed and how that would affect how people saw me. Maybe I just thought about it more deeply. I felt I wasn't giving 100 per cent of myself – I was OK with the singing and I tried my best with the dancing, but I definitely kept back some of myself. I knew for a fact I could be in a band, but whether I could be in the *Popstars* band was the big question.

'Maybe deep down I felt I didn't fit in because I didn't jump around in front of the cameras, but then I was getting down to the last few so I thought the judges must like me. I think I did wonder whether I should try to be more like some of the others. I didn't want to be in "presenter mode" and now I think that some people would have got further if they'd been themselves rather than acting the goat. At the end of the day I think it came down to a voice they were looking for and maybe a character.

'At the party they had for everyone who'd got to London there were cameras all over and people doing back flips and getting up to do karaoke. I didn't even get up and sing that night because to me that was chill-out time. I didn't know what the judges were looking for but if they wanted me to be the way some people were acting it was pointless. People were going to town that night and I just sat there and thought, "Maybe that's what they're looking for." It turned out they weren't. It wasn't the Kids From Fame. It was about real life.'

Kym: 'We had some good fun together, certainly at the beginning. They were filming all the time and we didn't know what they would end up using. A lot of it I couldn't even remember when I saw the shows. So much had happened you just forgot a lot of it – like the fake kiss between me and Noel, which was quite funny. When we saw that in the show we both looked at each other and went, "No-o-o!"'

Noel: 'The first few days in the house I didn't sleep very well. I remember being freaked out because Danny wasn't eating. I think it was just because he wasn't comfortable with the situation and that was his way of dealing with it.'

Danny: 'I think the *Popstars* people wanted a few fireworks and fall-outs, but generally I think people liked what they saw. We were five kids with a great opportunity – and maybe the audience liked that. I don't think people watching necessarily wanted to see arguments, but I think the powers-that-be probably thought it would be good to see us fighting and making up. The hardest thing for us was keeping it all a secret. I think we all felt we'd achieved something, got into the band, and we wanted to tell the world, but there was no way we could do that. We just had to disappear. I think it was harder for our families because they were being asked about us all the time and having to cover up.'

Myleene: 'Keeping everything secret in the beginning was horrible. I always said I wasn't going to lie. I hate lies. All my friends were ringing up wanting to know if I was in the band, and I just had to keep saying I was really busy.'

Danny: 'Keeping secrets makes me feel guilty, so I don't do it. My family had to cover for me when I disappeared but it was really difficult for them. I felt guilty about that. There were friends I never told and I felt bad about that. There's still a couple of friends I haven't been able to sit down and chat to about it and I think they found it hard that I wasn't able to trust them enough to tell them at the time.'

Suzanne: 'The most difficult thing during the early days was that I couldn't tell anyone what was happening. I couldn't share the excitement because no one knew I was in the band. It was hard being hidden away. It got to the point where the press had found out where we were and we just wanted everything to be out in the open. No one knew where all the press stories were coming from and Nigel came to the house and really got heavy. He told us if one of the band was leaking stuff then we'd be out.

'That was a really unpleasant time. They put the fear of God into us. They actually pointed the finger at me, sat me down and said they thought I was the leak – this was all done on camera. I was really scared Nigel was going to boot me out of the band. I was so stunned, crying my eyes out. I knew I hadn't said anything. Myleene sat me down and said it was all drama for the cameras and not to take it to heart. But I felt like I'd finally got what I wanted in life and someone was threatening to take it away from me. It was the scariest thing. Thankfully, the guys were behind me and it got to the point where we said that if one went we'd all go. Nigel told us not to be ridiculous and let one person spoil it for everyone, but that's how we felt.

'Afterwards I was so mad about it. We found out where the leak was coming from and it wasn't one of us. I thought, "How could they set me up like that for the cameras?

The people to impress – Nigel, Nicki and Paul.

Why me?" It was just for a bit of drama. I think they felt it was getting quite boring, we were all getting on too well, so Nigel had to come in and stir the whole thing up. They never showed the stuff on TV where they were pointing the finger at me because they knew I wasn't the leak.'

Myleene: 'I think the most pressure I've ever felt was when we were living as a group in secret. When they pointed the finger at Suzy it was a case of if she goes we all go. I remember being told I was being foolish to give up a chance like this, but I felt strongly that if we didn't all stand together there was no chance.'

Noel: 'There were stories in the paper and they weren't coming from any of us, but they had to make good telly and it's really weird to look back on that now. Everyone in the band honoured their contracts. My family knew what I was doing and a few close friends, but they were people I'd have trusted with my life. I probably told more people than I should have but it was impossible not to because I'd just disappeared. I had to say something. For them to point the finger at one of us was outrageous. We'd also been told that no other *Popstars* band had made it without one person being sacked, so there was the fear that one of us would go.

'After a few episodes we felt there was no way they could sack one of us, especially after we'd got through a lot of the recording. The record company had all our voices and there wouldn't have been time to record new ones.'

Danny: 'I thought they were wrong to point the finger and I remember feeling a bit of animosity towards Lythgoe because he'd come into our house and said all this stuff. Fair enough, the leak could have come from us or from the production team, but I thought that was all about creating a bit of drama for the programme. Afterwards, we decided to stick together as a five. If one went, we all did. You have to stick together as a group, and we've always banged on about that, but that's why we've come so far so quickly. That's why it works.'

Kym: 'I think that's why Nigel was there – to build the drama. We weren't interested in fighting or falling out, so I think they pushed issues to make it more dramatic. They had an image of each of us – I was the noisy one, Noel was the funny mummy's boy, Danny was the smiler who cried all the time. It wasn't true, but that's the power of editing. I think there was good and bad in the whole thing. People saw what made us cry, they saw what made us laugh and now they think they know what makes us tick. To a degree we're the people's band. People feel they know us, and that's nice.'

Danny: 'I remember the morning Kiss 100 turned up on the doorstep. Me and Noel were upstairs leaning over the banister, listening. That was when it all went a bit pear-shaped. We left the house that day and went to see our lawyer, and we were snapped by the paparazzi. Then we went to LWT and stayed there for hours. We weren't allowed to go back to the house. It was a depressing time.'

Myleene: 'We hadn't been revealed as a band but the press had found the house. We left the house not knowing we wouldn't be able to go back. All we had was what we

Concentrating hard...Danny learns a new song.

2.0

were standing up in. Someone else had to go back and pack our stuff into black bin liners. I had to ask someone to go through my personal things and that was intrusive and horrible. I remember sitting in this room at LWT and looking round at everyone's faces and just thinking, "My God, what are we doing?" They took our mobile phones off us because a journalist had got the numbers, so we couldn't even ring our families.

'That was such a low point. The first night we couldn't go back to the house we ended up staying with friends of Nigel. We were staying with people we didn't even know. We stayed in three different houses in the space of a week. I remember being quite scared at the scale of all the press interest and thinking, "This must be really big."'

Suzanne: 'We moved without warning into a totally different house. We were living out of bin liners and we didn't have our things around us. I remember feeling really ill because we never saw daylight. When we went out we had to wear masks and indoors we had the curtains drawn the whole time. I was still happy about being in the band but I just wanted them to let people know who we were. I thought if people were trying so hard to find us then *Popstars* was going to be a huge hit.'

Kym: 'When we had to move out, that was when I cracked up. I couldn't ring my children, there were reporters everywhere, we were wearing masks, running, hiding. Then they moved us to a house in a terraced row in Archway, in North London. When I saw it I just flipped. I was sure the press would find us, but luckily they didn't. It was a very tough time.

Danny has a break and tries to absorb the incredible events of the previous weeks.

Nigel with Noel, Kym and Myleene.

'I think that was the lowest point because I couldn't speak to my children for two days and that was hell. I still find it hard to accept that my children aren't with me twenty-four/seven. It's very difficult. I still miss them as much as I did in the beginning but I accept the fact it isn't for ever and I'm doing the right thing. There were times when I wondered about that and worried they would hate me or forget about me. If there was ever the danger of that happening I would go straight away, but they're happy and they love me and that's all that matters. When we're together we're just us and nothing has changed. I think kids can cope with a lot more than people think.'

Danny: 'We lost our house, we lost our phones, we had no clothes. At that point the only people keeping us together were our families and we couldn't even speak to them, so it was really grim. Then we moved into the house in Archway for a while. We were just watching our backs all the time. The mood between us was fine. It was one of those experiences that made us stronger because we were on the run and it was just the five of us together.'

Suzanne: 'It was very difficult being hidden away. I was very shocked at how much interest there was. I remember when we first encountered the paparazzi outside our lawyer's office and suddenly there were cameras in our faces. It was exciting but I was shaking as well.'

Myleene: 'That was the pressure week. I'd had a call from the "Inland Revenue" and it turned out to be a journalist. My mum was getting calls from the press and people knocking at the door every day. She had one call saying I was seriously ill in hospital, and she couldn't contact me. She was so worried. They had to bring forward the

TIME CHECK

Kym's favourtie song, Back for Good by Take That, was one of their eight number ones. A great target for Hear'say to hit!

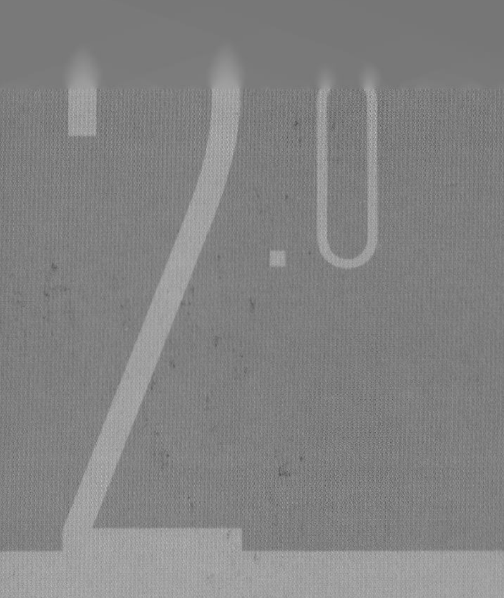

Our first day in the house.

show revealing the band by a week because it was all too much. Our families were going through hell. One thing the experience taught me was that I'm a lot stronger than I realized.'

Kym: 'That episode of the show when we moved was a bad one for me because I flipped over the new house, I flipped with the girls and I flipped at Nigel saying I needed to lose weight. All that came out in one week on TV. Nigel had really touched my Achilles heel. He knew I was worried about my weight, we'd had conversations about it. He used to ask me why I was worried, then all of a sudden he's telling me – on screen – I'm fat. Eleven million viewers saw that and it was very embarrassing and I was very upset. I let rip – at him and then at Myleene, although I apologized to her afterwards. Even though we'd talked about it, I don't think Nigel understood just how upsetting it would be for me.

'I think that show was very good for me in some ways and very damaging in others because people – especially younger people – didn't realize why I reacted the way I did. I think Nigel's remarks were unpopular and a lot of people rallied behind me, but some just saw me as a nasty person who shouted at everyone. It was quite upsetting because after that I wasn't as popular as I had been. I think I'm making up for that now. I can't tell you how many people I've met who say, "Actually you're really nice." When we get asked if Nigel was really nasty I always want to say YES because he was. Of course we've got him to thank for *Popstars* but there are ways of going about things and that was so wrong.'

Noel: 'We were doing alright for a while managing ourselves, but then one day four of us were ill when we were meant to be recording. We knew it was pointless going into the studio because we couldn't sing and we'd just have had to go back and do it all again. We had the TV company on our case, the *Popstars* director was chasing us, wanting to know where we were, we had the studio on our case and the record company. We realized we needed someone else to handle that stuff. We didn't really know what we were looking for in a manager. We needed someone with experience and a decent track record ... and when we couldn't find anyone like that we settled for Chris Herbert! Just kidding!'

Myleene: 'We had to learn a lot fast. I can remember thinking, Oh my God – we need a manager. We were trying to handle the politics of it all ourselves. I had a basic idea of how to deal with lawyers and read a contract because I'd done that before, but we had to think about everything. What was important was the recording side of things, but we'd be worrying because only one car had turned up and it didn't have blacked-out windows. Most of this job is dealing with people. It's ten per cent music, ninety per cent politics, dealing with producers, the record company, making sure everyone's happy. We have always had a lot of leeway. If we don't like a song we'll say so. We don't sing songs we don't like, which is amazing. There are bands that have no choice. I know some bands are told what to sing, what to wear, what to eat, and that doesn't happen with us. We've got common sense on our side and we all bring something to the band. If you put all the experience together, it's valuable. There's always one of us who can deal with whatever is going on.

'When it comes to styling I think it was probably more nerve-racking for the stylists than us because we do have a lot of say. We knew we had to be daring in some respects and wear things that aren't already out there, but the clothes have to be the kind of things you'd wear anyway. Let's just say you wouldn't get me in a ball gown. I was sitting in a restaurant the other day with Noel and there was a girl dressed in a Hear'say outfit. I never thought we had such a specific look, but she had her studded belt worn to the side, she had the slashed T-shirt and the jeans. I just thought, "*Ohmygod!*" I never imagined that happening – but then all kinds of strange things have happened. We've got a tribute band and our song has been played on *EastEnders*, which tells you you've made it. All I need now is for someone to name their baby after me!'

The house was always full of music.

FAMOUS FIVE

3

Suzanne: 'Looking back, I seemed so young and naive. I was quite fazed by it all. It was like a dream and we were just thrown into things without time to think about it.'

3.0

Kym: 'It was such a relief to be revealed because we'd begun to feel caged. There was so much we couldn't do, like go to the supermarket. I actually remember the night we were revealed because we were in Norway, recording at Stargate. We'd brought the video of the show with us and we watched it at the same time as everyone in the UK. I was the first one to be shown and I ran round the studios, screaming. Then my mum rang me and she was screaming. It was as if I'd just found out, but what made it exciting was that now everyone else knew too. It was like getting your freedom back.'

Danny: 'When we were in Norway before the band was revealed we were able to relax a bit, but even there the paparazzi were after us. They knew we were recording at Stargate, so it was a bit nerve-racking. When we came back to do our first press conference at Heathrow we didn't know what to expect. I don't think anyone knew how many people would be there, but the good thing for us was that the secrecy was over.'

Suzanne: 'At that first press conference I felt I'd got what I always wanted – all these people were interested in me. It was my dream come true and I had a big beaming smile on my face. The whole thing was absolutely amazing. Yes, they did slag off my hair extensions, but because I was so happy it didn't bother me. I knew I could do something with my hair. The whole thing was so exciting, amazing. It was an extraordinary turn-out. I had this constant giggle inside that wouldn't go away.'

Noel: 'I was so nervous when I got off the coach and saw all the photographers. Then we went into this room that was full of journalists and camera crews. It was really scary – the whole media machine is really bizarre. I remember afterwards reading pieces that said we came out with spoon-fed lines and that we had perfectly rehearsed Bridge Over Troubled Water, which we sang. We actually weren't trained to say anything, we just used our common sense. And we hadn't rehearsed – we were just always singing as a five, in the house or in the car. That was the extent of our rehearsal.'

Trying out a new song for the first time.

Myleene: 'I remember our press officer saying it was the biggest turn-out they'd ever seen for any band. When we got off the coach and saw the cameras we were all pinching ourselves. It was like, "I just don't get this." We were nervous but we had a job to do and in a sense it's an easy job because it's just about being yourself.'

Danny: 'We knew we had to go out and see whether or not they liked us – that was the bottom line. The press could have been really vile and shot us down in flames, but in general it was quite positive. We were told that the press conference was very quiet. We didn't know because we'd never done one before.'

Kym: 'We didn't have a clue what to expect. I think they tried to give us an idea at the *Popstars* auditions but I don't think any of us were prepared. The funny thing was we thought they'd be firing questions about this and that and they didn't really ask us very much. They seemed stunned. They were just looking at us. I don't know if they were trying to weigh us up or what. They were a lot easier on us than they

might have been. I was expecting really personal, prying questions, so I was quite nervous, but I was also excited to be part of it. I think we handled the questions well. They probably all thought we'd done loads of media training but we'd only had one afternoon. That was quite funny. I remember Chris Herbert, our manager, saying he couldn't believe how well we'd handled it. We were really pleased. I think we've had to take everything in our stride. If we were fazed we couldn't do our job.'

Myleene: 'You can't be taught to deal with the media, not really. Our media training was literally about sitting up straight, not slouching, being told to stick to the questions and not go off on a tangent, that kind of stuff. We had a three-hour session and that's not exactly an education. People somehow think the answers are fed to you. I wish someone *was* there helping us, because so many times I don't have the answers. In a way, I think people appreciate our honesty.'

Danny: 'We didn't have any textbook answers. All we could do was go out there and be ourselves. People thought we'd had so much media training but we didn't and I think that was a bonus. Looking out at that room full of journalists, you don't know if they're out to get you, but it went well. We were on *News at Ten* – that was major!'

Noel: 'I think *Popstars* was our media training, spending all that time in front of the cameras. Cameras don't intimidate me any more, yet that was the most harrowing thing about the auditions.'

We arrive at Heathrow with no real idea what to expect.

It was so strange to see ourselves on the front page of The Sun.

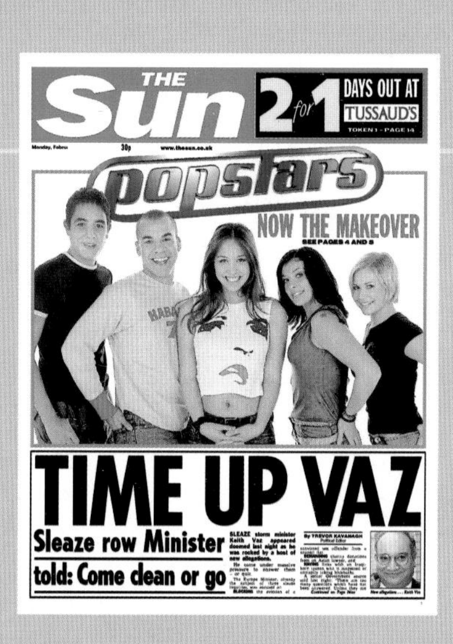

THE Sun

2 for 1 DAYS OUT AT TUSSAUDS

popstars

NOW THE MAKEOVER

TIME UP VAZ

Sleaze row Minister told: Come clean or go

3.0

And the band is ...
we keep the suspense going.

At last! We can stop hiding.

Suzanne: 'We went straight from the press conference to do our first major shoot for ten magazine covers. Looking back, I seemed so young and naïve. I was quite fazed by it all. It was like a dream and we were just thrown into things without time to think about it. Everything we did was over before it had time to sink in. I think that's how we coped with a lot of stuff.'

Kym: 'There has been so much press. Good or bad, that's what's made us. If people weren't talking about us, if they didn't find us interesting, if they weren't concerned about who we were seeing, there would be something wrong. I never imagined myself on the cover of *Marie Claire* or *GQ* magazine. When we went into this whole thing we didn't know how big it would be so all that is a surprise.'

Myleene: 'So many covers stand out for me – *NME*, *The Face*, *GQ* ... and *Marie Claire* because I always used to buy it and I kept every issue in a pile under my bed. Now I'm on the covers of the magazines I used to read. I'm on the programmes I used to watch as a kid. I'm in *the* pop band and it's an extraordinary life. Whatever happens, Hear'say will be remembered. Something massive has happened in our lives and yet we haven't even clocked it properly. It's not normal. It's everything I wanted but I can't believe I've got it. There's not one second when I feel I would like my old life back.'

Noel: 'The magazine covers I really remember are *NME* and *The Face* because you wouldn't expect to find a pop band on the front of those. I also remember the *Sun* with the five of us on the front page. That was amazing, but it's also strange. You pick up a magazine with your face on it and you think it's just for you. You don't think about other people seeing it or buying it.'

Suzanne: 'When I went home for Easter my mum had kept every newspaper and she gave me this huge book of cuttings. I sat down and read them all and that's when I realized how big this whole thing is. It's huge. That was a really big reality check for me. We've had so many great magazine covers, but I loved the *Smash Hits* one with me and Noel kissing. They called us the king and queen of pop – as if! I loved the *GQ* cover and the *Popstars* magazine cover with us all holding the exploding TV. That is really memorable.'

Danny: 'Me and Myleene went into a shop one day and there were all these magazines with us on the cover. *cdUK* had me and Noel on the front, *Top of the Pops* magazine had Noel solo, the girls were on *GQ*, and *TV Hits* had Noel, Suzanne and me. We were just buying a packet of crisps like anyone else and there were all these magazines. When I went home at Easter there was a Hear'say billboard right next to my old secondary school. I went to the pub and I could see it from there. It was so weird. I had to ring the others and tell them their faces were staring down at me.'

A couple of our most memorable covers.

With Paul and Nicki at the Press Conference. You can tell how relieved we are.

Myleene: 'I used to collect sticker books and now there's one of us. I bought Danny a birthday card with him and Noel on the front. You just pinch yourself and think, "What's that about?" It's very bizarre.'

Suzanne: 'I don't think all the press attention has stopped us doing normal things. People are comfortable with us, they feel they know us, so we don't tend to get hassle. I can go clubbing and nobody will really pay any attention. I go to the supermarket on my own, I still shop in Top Shop. I haven't been on the Tube, I'm not sure about that.'

Noel: 'You find that if you're looking busy and getting on with things, people don't tend to bother you. If you're wandering round aimlessly, that's when you get stopped, so I tend to zoom around a bit now.'

Myleene: 'I do all the things I did before. I still get the Tube because it's quicker. I still jump on a bus to get from one end of Oxford Street to the other. You do get guidance from management and the record company on what you can and can't do, but usually your best counsel is your own. I'd always be wary if I was on a beach because there'd probably be a photographer somewhere, but you just learn to live with that. We're in an unusual position. People have seen us go through this audition process, they've seen us struggle, and they feel they know us. There's this whole thing of celebrity that is untouchable and remote, but reality TV has taken fame full circle. Now we all like the idea of normal people who get up there and prove they can do it. Everyone knows someone like us and the idea that it *is* possible is what captured people's interest. It's wicked. I know if I hadn't been in the band I'd have still been watching *Popstars* and thinking, "Good for you."'

Danny: 'The only thing I haven't done is been on the Tube, and I miss it. It's such a busy place and if someone had a go at you there's really no escape. I've been really lucky, although I've had odd bits of abuse. I don't see why I should take abuse now because I certainly wouldn't have before. One night I was in a really busy bar in Hoxton Square and everyone was standing shoulder to shoulder. I was thinking it maybe wasn't a good place to be, then this girl came up and said someone had written on my back. I thought she was joking with me. What had happened was

Having a laugh at our first press conference.

someone had tried to write a four-letter word on my jacket in felt-tip pen. I'm so glad I didn't see it happening because I'd have said something and it could have been a nasty situation.'

Myleene: 'I remember saying, "We won't change" – and we haven't. It's the people around you. They get an idea in their head that you're a different person so when they meet you they treat you differently. I was in the toilet queue at the airport and there must have been about twenty people in front of me. I was just standing at the back, reading my Harry Potter book, and this woman came up and tapped me on the shoulder. She said, "I hope you don't expect to get preferential treatment." I said, "Well, if I did, I wouldn't be standing at the back of the queue." I was so annoyed. Sometimes you can't win.'

Kym: 'Before, being a pop star was the dream, and now that's the reality. So now what we dream about is doing normal things. When I went home for David's sports day it was a chance for me to be normal, but even then I was signing autographs. By the end of the day every kid's T-shirt had "lots of love, Kym" on it. I don't

Three ... two ... one ...
That countdown to hear whether we'd made it to number one was so nerve-racking!

complain about it because the people you're signing for are the people who've helped us get where we are today.'

Danny: 'There was a rumour going round that we were going to perform at the Brits and someone came down to the studio where we were rehearsing to watch us. He must have liked what he saw because the week before the show we were told we were going to be on. Chris Herbert, our manager, came to Ray Hedges' studio in Surrey where we were finishing off some tracks for the album to tell us. I went, 'No-o-o!' – as usual. It was just mad. We were warned we'd get people booing us but it didn't really matter. We already had a good record company, so the thought of other record companies booing us didn't mean a lot. When we went on and looked down there were all these kids singing "Pure And Simple" – and it hadn't even been released! Afterwards we felt really good. We came off stage, got changed and literally got into two cars and went off to start our radio tour. There was no party, nothing.'

The most incredible moment of our lives. Pure and Simple is number one!

Kym: 'We hadn't even had a single out and we knew we weren't welcomed by a lot of people at the Brits. We were just TV faces at that time as far as they were concerned – we hadn't earned the right to be there. For us, the show is a celebration of British

music and that's what we were about and working towards. We got up there and sang and there were boos from the record industry, but we'd been warned about that. It was a big night and there was lots of hustle and bustle going on, a few nerves on edge but it was generally a good atmosphere. It's such a huge venue. When we walked on stage I was so scared. I almost fainted at one point. It's one of the worst feelings I've ever had, walking out there and not knowing how people would receive us. Inside I was crumbling – I just did a good job of hiding it.'

Danny: 'We didn't know for a while that "Pure And Simple" was going to be the first single but it was just so anthemic – it just felt like it was the one. I wasn't sure it was going to be a number one but it was getting a lot of radio play and I thought it would be top ten, so that was good. The day we got to number one I remember arriving back at the house and finding LWT had taken over the place. They'd tidied up (!) and everyone was waiting for Davina McCall to arrive. Our families were there and we just went and got ready for the show. When we heard we'd got to number one we just went mad. To be honest, being in that room with our families, it didn't matter whether we'd made it or not – we'd achieved something, and it was quite emotional.

Meeting our dolls for the first time!

It all got a bit much for David and Emily.

3.0

TIME CHECK

Exactly one year before Pure and Simple shot to number one, Chicane topped the charts with Don't Give Up – very appropriate!

(right and far right) While we were recording Pure and Simple, we had no idea how successful it would be.

'Getting to number one wasn't actually the pinnacle for me. If I'm really honest, it was the small things, like being in the car together and hearing the song played on the radio that meant the most. Just having a single out was the coolest thing. That's what mattered to me. We'd worked so hard. I remember going home and sitting having fish and chips with my nan and granddad and watching *Top of the Pops* with Richard Blackwood introducing us as "the hardest-working band in pop". That's when it hits you.'

Kym: 'The day Pure And Simple went to number one on March 18th was really special. I've got that show on video and every now and then I watch it. We'd been in the recording studio in the morning and came home starving hungry. Our families were there and I remember Emily, my three-year-old, was cranky. We were all eating pizzas on the run and getting ready for the live show that evening. It was havoc in the house. There were people I'd never seen before and cameras everywhere. Outside, there were police and barriers. It was the strangest day and also the greatest day for me.

'When it got to number two on the chart rundown and we heard "Uptown Girl" we all just screamed. It was an amazing feeling, very moving, although I couldn't cry. I was just too shocked and surprised. It was only later, when the cameras had gone, that you sit there and go, "Ohmygod, what have we done? Wow!" That's when I started crying. We went to bed very late and then just tossed and turned all night.'

Noel: 'We were all standing there listening to the countdown and when they told us how many we had sold in that first week – 549,839 – it didn't sink in. I still don't get it now. You're listening to this radio broadcast and I remember thinking it was just Mark Goodier telling us in our house – not that there were millions of people watching it all. It didn't feel real. People tell you you've sold so many singles on the first day, then in the first week, and it's just overwhelming. I'm sure in about a year's time I'll go, "Wow, that's excellent."

'But it all happens so fast and then you move on to the next thing. You do a big show then you're in a car and off somewhere else. You don't have time to relax and enjoy it. It's very hectic and I think that's why we've coped so well. We don't have time to linger on things. We just keep going.'

Suzanne: 'I was hoping it would get into the top five. To have so much success so fast was amazing. We never dreamed we'd have the fastest-selling debut single ever. Even now, I wonder if all that really happened. It's unreal, except I know it's not because I've got a platinum disc to go on the wall of my flat, so that's proof if I ever need it that we sold over a million copies. I'll never get bored of hearing "Pure And Simple". I love it.'

Myleene: '"Pure And Simple" was such a great song. It represented so much. We'd beaten off Nigel. We'd won our battles with our nerves. There was a sense of having struggled and having this anthem that just epitomized the whole thing. When we sang it at the Rugby League Challenge Cup Final at Twickenham in April, that was one of the best feelings ever. No one wanted us to sing live because it was a huge stadium and the weather was bad but in the end we sang in the rain and the crowd sang with us. I looked like a drowned rat but I remember being so proud of what we'd done. It was amazing. Tony Blair was there and afterwards we met him. It was so funny! No one knew how many copies that single would sell but now we're in the *Guinness Book of Records*. We're part of history and no one can ever take that away.'

Danny: 'People ask what it's like, being famous, and it's pretty much the same as before except a lot more people know you. In a weird kind of way *Popstars* has made it easier for me to deal with fame because the show allowed us to be ourselves.'

Noel: 'The next time they do *Popstars* people will know what to expect. It will be bigger and better. People will know how to act to get noticed. I think the one thing we had was our naïvete, which was so obvious. You can see how we've changed and to some extent become hardened to it all, but we were always able to be ourselves, which is a blessing because now we don't have to play a part.'

KISS AND TELL

4

Myleene: 'Everyone warns you about the press. It's not the press, it's the people who betray you that you have to worry about.'

WARNING
save £60 on your car insurance
0800 300 300
All tickets half price.
All tickets half price.
(Just to save you looking twice.)
Waterhouse
A boost for the Piggybank People
Fury at speed cameras plan for all roads

TIME CHECK

Noel was born in the Summer of 1980, forty summers earlier another Welsh hero was born – Mr Tom Jones

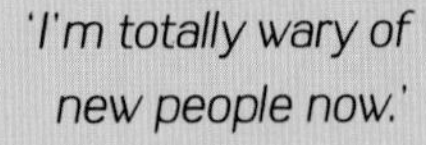

'I'm totally wary of new people now.'

Noel: 'I never really wanted the fame thing. A lot of the time the press seem more interested in who you're in bed with or who you fancy than when the next single's coming out. They supported us all the way through *Popstars* and helped make us, but now I feel like the good stories about us are getting fewer and fewer.'

Suzanne: 'The first bad story that appeared in the papers about me called me "a scheming pop tart". The cameras were on me when I read that, which made it feel a lot worse than it actually was, but I remember thinking people would read the story and hate me. I was accused of stealing a girl's boyfriend, and it was nothing like that. That was during *Popstars*. They'd keep the papers from us until the cameras were there then say, "What do you think of that?" You didn't get a chance to sit down and think, "Hold on, what's the reality here?" The general reaction to that first story was that people didn't actually believe it. Looking back, it seems like nothing now. A lot more has happened since.'

Kym: 'My relationship with my boyfriend Martin lasted eighteen months. We got engaged at Christmas, although I never wanted to but he asked me in front of people and I found it difficult to say no. I think he did it for his own reasons. Before *Popstars* and all this he was never interested in settling down. Looking back, I think getting engaged was either about him feeling better because I was committed to him, or about wanting to be engaged to a pop star. On the whole, I think it was the latter because of what happened later when he sold his story to a newspaper.

'We were going through a rocky patch because I couldn't see him very much and he needed me because his mum was ill. She had bowel cancer while the whole *Popstars* auditions process was going on and I sat with him, held his hand, cried with him. I was very close to his mum, I loved her. She seemed to be doing well, then she was diagnosed again a couple of months before we split up. It was really upsetting. He needed me but I couldn't get to see him because I was working, and when I did have time off I wanted to see my children, so it was becoming a problem. The attraction was wearing off for me. I felt I couldn't stay with him just because I felt sorry for him. I knew there was never going to be a right time to break up. I just had to do what I felt was right, so I finished with him.

'Just before we split up he'd said he was going to have to talk to the press because they wouldn't leave him alone, but that he wouldn't say anything bad about me, so I said okay. Once we'd split I assumed he wouldn't talk to the newspapers, but he did. The story that appeared was really bad. It was such a shock to me. When I opened the paper and saw it I was gutted because this was the guy I'd thought I would be with for a while. I really thought I knew him, but clearly I didn't.

'Before I did *Popstars* I thought money would make me happy, but it's not money – it's what you're doing that makes you happy. That's a big lesson I've learned. To me, money is the root of all evil. All I'll say to the people who've sold stories about us is that I hope the money makes them happy, because once it runs out they'll find they have very little.'

Myleene: 'I had to tell my mum not to react, no matter what anyone said. I told her that she would hear awful things. One journalist asked if I was from a broken home

Noel and Suzanne check out yet another story.

because my dad's away a lot. Mainly, the upheavals have been when people sell stories. Before all this I was really trusting and then a topless picture of me on holiday appeared in a Sunday paper. I'd forgotten all about that picture. It was actually a picture of a rock and I was just a dot in the sea. Of course, they blew it up so it looked like it was just a picture of me. I was eighteen years old when it was taken and suddenly I was trying to justify myself to people. It was a horrible feeling. When Suzy came to tell me there was a topless picture of me in the paper I just laughed, but she was serious.

'When I saw it the first thing I wanted to do was ring my brother and tell him to get hold of all the papers from the newsagents. I didn't want my parents to see it. When I spoke to him I hadn't realized my mum had picked up the line at the same time and she could hear me telling him to go and buy up all the papers. My mum just said, "Whatever it is, you're our baby." I burst into tears. It was an ex-boyfriend who sold that picture, someone I'd known for nearly five years. I trusted him and he betrayed me.

'Everyone warns you about the press. It's not the press, it's the people who betray you that you have to worry about.'

Suzanne: 'I'm always looking round to see if there are photographers hiding in the bushes. When I was on holiday I couldn't relax because I was convinced they were there – and they were. I had three different bikinis with me and they had pictures of me on different days wearing each one. You sometimes wonder how you can live your life like that, but it goes with the territory. Every time I go on stage I know that's why I'm doing this, and that's what counts. Open-air gigs are amazing. I get a shiver

'It's not the press, it's the people who betray you that you have to worry about.'

'I am more cynical now, and that bothers me.'

down my back and feel like I'm about to cry. It's such a buzz. But then you come off stage and the press want to ask about Andrew, my boyfriend, or what I think of such-and-such a story about me. It has made me more cynical and that bothers me. I'm getting to the stage where I don't really ring my friends any more because people have sold stories and I'm wary. I wonder if it's going to keep on happening and if I'll end up as a recluse. It sounds stupid, but I think about that.'

TIME CHECK
Abba's Eurovision winner Waterloo was in 1974, seven years before Suzanne was born!

Myleene: 'For a while I was scared of being lonely because I'd pick up the paper and see someone else had sold me out and I'd think, "My God, am I going to lose all my friends?" But that was just a momentary scare. The friends that have stuck with me are amazing. And I've got the best friends I could have in the band. They're more like family. Because we've been through so much together I believe there is something big between us now. People say they can feel it when they meet us. We know each other so well – Noel and Danny have morphed into each other.'

Noel: 'I'm totally wary of new people, you have to be. I watch what I say in front of people I don't know. You never know if they're going to go to the papers. There's nothing people like more than to say "I met so-and-so and he was nasty". They may have caught you in a snippet of your day when you're not at your best. We all have those moments. The worst thing about stories appearing is that sometimes you don't know who sold them and maybe that person is still around. I'm in the position now where maybe I won't be able to trust people for the next couple of years or so. It's not something I like to dwell on, but I can't see myself forming new attachments or relationships at the moment. Anyway, I'm having trouble keeping up with my family and my old friends without letting new people into my life.'

Myleene: 'I'm wary of people now and that's awful. I find it hard to trust people and that's unfair – why should they have to prove themselves? As far as I'm concerned, forget money, looks, everything. If you haven't got integrity you've got nothing.'

Suzanne: 'The papers are under pressure to find stories. Sometimes they offer a lot of money – and some people feel it doesn't matter if they tell. They think you're doing all right, earning money, and they just want a little bit.'

Kym: 'There are people who've been friends for years who you could trust in the past. You could tell them a secret and they'd keep it because there was nothing to gain from telling anyone. Then a newspaper comes along and offers them thousands of pounds for that secret. They think it's going to make them happy and it doesn't. There have been times when I've picked up a paper and gone, "What the —?" But I do try and let most of it go.'

Myleene: 'There are so few people you can trust and you could never put a price on loyalty. People don't realize that money doesn't buy happiness.'

Suzanne: 'You can never be prepared for what might appear in the press. We were told so many times that the tabloids would try and find out every little thing about us. I thought, okay, I'm prepared for that. But then you get a phone call from someone saying, "You won't like what's in the paper about you this morning," like I did when my dad called me to tell me about the "ex-boyfriend" story. Luckily, it was

'I never sit with my back to the door now.'

brushed aside, but it did hurt my feelings. I'm not usually someone who cries. I let things build up to the point where I suddenly explode and then I cry. People think I'm strong but behind closed doors I have my tears.

'I've had three horrible articles in the papers so far. When my ex-boyfriend sold a story, it was utter stupidity. I was with him for two years and I thought he was a lovely guy. The week before the story appeared he told me he couldn't believe that people were selling stuff about me. A week later his story appeared in the *News of the World*, then in the *Sport*.'

Danny: 'I've always said when you get to this point it's very hard to complain about media intrusion. People are interested in us because they feel they know us, but I'm sure there is a fine line. I like reading positive interviews but when you read negative stuff, or lies, that is crossing the line. I don't think you can really understand it until it's directed at you, and I don't fully understand it because it hasn't happened to me. I haven't really had any negative stories. I'll always be there for the others and I feel sad and upset for them, but I don't really understand what it's like to look at a newspaper and see yourself portrayed in a way you wanted to forget about. The others have all been betrayed by friends and that hasn't happened to me, although I think there have been plenty of attempts by journalists to dig up dirt on me.'

Suzanne: 'My family hasn't really been bothered by all the media attention surrounding us and I'm glad about that, but Andrew, my boyfriend, has had a lot of reporters on the doorstep. He went through a phase where he was getting calls from the press every day. Even recently, he had a call saying I was seeing someone else because a reporter had seen a friend call at my flat. The worrying thing is it's not just me that gets hurt – it's my family and friends too.

We were warned that the tabloid attention would be tough.

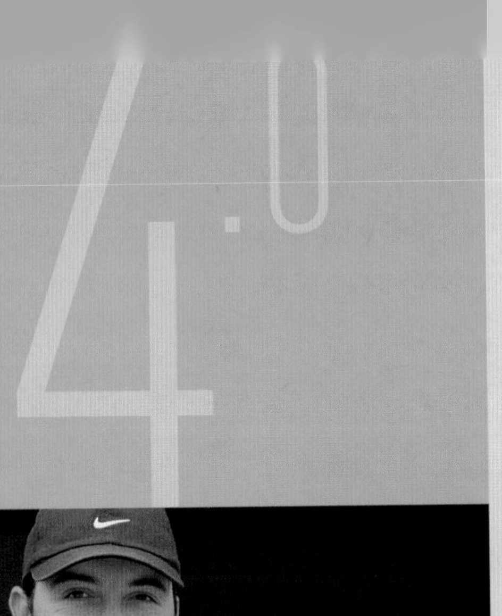

'I've had a story posted on a website saying I've committed suicide. There was also a story saying I'd been electrocuted on the video shoot for our second single. It's nasty stuff, and now I've started getting horrible hate mail. There have been three letters sent to my mum and dad saying really awful things about me and threatening to kill me. The person sending them must be very disturbed. I've handed them over our lawyer. To put up with stuff like that when all you want is to do the job you love is harsh.

'For years all I've wanted is to be famous, and suddenly you realize there's a flip side and that can be really depressing. Luckily, I've got a strong family and a really good boyfriend who does his best to support me. If I didn't have that, I'm sure I would take it harder.'

Both Suzanne's ex-boyfriend and Andrew's ex-girlfriend sold stories about them.

Noel: 'People are different with me now I'm in the public eye – they wouldn't speak to me before! People you haven't seen for a while don't know how to take you anymore. The other day I met up with one of my mates and she had a friend with her I hadn't seen since school. This girl was saying, "How am I going to be with him? What am I going to say?" That's not normal. It's not really about you, it's about how other people deal with the situation. They view you differently.'

Suzanne: 'I do think I've changed. When I look back to the auditions and to our first appearance on *Top of the Pops* I looked so young for my age and just so happy. Now I feel like I look a lot older and I'm a lot more cynical and much more aware of what's going on around me. For the first time I feel I'm getting bags under my eyes. When I was eighteen I was auditioning for parts for fifteen-year-olds and I could get away with it. I don't feel I could now. Looking back, I can't believe how naive we all were.'

Kym: 'I feel I've changed. I think I've aged. I know it sounds silly and people tell me I'm still a baby but I'm twenty-five and to me that's five years off thirty. I look for grey hairs. *Popstars* started my ageing process. When I look back at photographs of us when we went to record with Elliot Kennedy, who was the first producer we worked with, we looked so young – so fresh-faced and bright-eyed. Now we can't have a picture taken, not even a normal family photo, without doing a pose. It's become second nature. It's as if now we're in Hear'say mode we find it difficult to step out of that.'

Noel: 'I have changed, but not in a bad way. It would be abnormal not to change under the circumstances. I find my ability to communicate with people is a lot better and my confidence has grown. I'm finally being recognized for doing something. We have to deal with things most people our age never have to think about. For most twenty-year-olds their concerns are doing their dissertation for college, or paying the electricity bill on their student house, or going out Friday night, spending Saturday recovering, and going down the pub on Sunday. I think it's good for us because you grow up a lot quicker, but I also think it's scary because we're going to look back and say, "Whoa – what happened to our lost teens?" I think I've become more cynical and harder, and I'm definitely a lot more tired!'

'I've learned that you can't trust everyone.'

4.0

As long as we stick together, we can cope.

(far right) The view from our side of the camera. Scary or what!

Kym: 'I think I'm a lot more cynical. I look at things in a different way. I think about everything inside out before making a decision and I don't take anything for granted. I've learned that you can't trust everyone. I think I'm a lot harder inside than I used to be, which is a good thing because for quite a long time I was a dithering wreck inside. I had frequent panic attacks whereas now, although I still get them, I can control them. I tend to get them if I'm really stressed or if I'm tired or upset. I also have to make sure I eat properly because if my blood-sugar level gets low I start to panic. Basically, I've learned how to deal with it. I think my panic attacks have held me back in the past. But I feel like I've had some breakthroughs recently. It might not seem like much, but I haven't been shopping by myself for about three years because I don't like being on my own. The other day I parked my car in Hampstead because I needed to go to the post office. I went in and thought, "Actually, this isn't bad." Normally I'm sweating and I can't cope but I felt really good. I went off and did some food shopping and I was fine. I never even used to drive my car by myself because my first panic attack was in a car while I was driving, so I associated them with that. Sometimes I get really nervous before we go on stage but I throw myself into the performance and then I don't have time to panic. I'm doing really well and that's down to Jack, my boyfriend, because he makes me so happy and I don't feel I have anything to worry about.'

Danny: 'I never sit with my back to a door now because I like to be able to see what's going on. The other day I was in a restaurant, having lunch with a friend, and there were two guys hanging round outside reading the menu. I recognized one of them – he was one of the paparazzi. I went out and said hello and he asked if he could take some photos. I just said, "Fine." Then it's just another picture of me smiling. Afterwards, I was trying to get a taxi and someone came up with a camcorder and started filming. It's strange but you can't be off about it, because you don't know if it's going to end up on a website or something.'

Myleene: 'Most of the time the stories in the press are fine. When you do see bad or hurtful stories you just have to learn to turn the page. I do read them but I've learned not to react.'

BREAKING EUROPE

5

Danny: 'It's a new market in Europe and that's good for you. You walk down the street and no one knows you, and it's a reminder that not everyone knows who Hear'say is. It also reminds you that nothing can be taken for granted and that you have to work every territory.'

Too late!
We missed the flight!

Noel: 'We'd all like to break Europe but we know how much hard work it's going to take so we don't expect anything to happen overnight. It's interesting when you go there because every country has its own *Popstars* and they've all been through the same experience as us. We went to Germany this year for a couple of days to do a TV show called *The Dome*, and some interviews, and we met the German *Popstars* band, No Angels. They were cool girls.'

Myleene: 'The day we went to Germany we all met up at Heathrow for an early flight to Munich. From there we had to make a connection to Leipzig. We all knew there wasn't much time to get to the Leipzig flight but we thought we'd make it – we're always optimistic! Then our plane took off late from London and we started to get a bit nervous. Once we landed at Munich we had to race through the terminal building, but by then we knew we were up against it.'

Noel: 'I knew we'd already missed the flight but everyone was still rushing through the terminal as if there was still a chance. The plane had gone! Myleene kept saying, "We might still make it!" I was falling about laughing. I just thought that was taking optimism a bit far. Then we got a bit lost and that was it really. By the time we got to the gate there was no one there. We ended up with hours to kill before the next flight. It took us nine hours to get to Leipzig, which is probably a record.'

TIME CHECK

German Popstars winners No Angel's new single, Rivers of Joy, charted at number 13 in Germany on 30 April this year.

Kym: 'We knew we were meant to go straight into make-up when we got to Leipzig because we had interviews to do. But the delay meant there wouldn't be time for that, so we did our own make-up while we were waiting for the flight. We can do our make-up anywhere now – on planes, in cars, wherever. We were all feeling good despite the early start and all the waiting round. Then the airport bus took us out to our next plane and I started to feel sick – it was this tiny little plane with propellers, and I am not the world's best flyer. It's a real phobia for me. I sat with Noel and he managed to calm me down, but I felt pretty nervous. I used to be a lot worse, but I've had to overcome it because I can't let my fear stop me from travelling.'

Danny: 'I love flying, especially if there's a bit of turbulence! The flight to Leipzig was horrendous, though. I don't know if it was just because it was a small plane but the pressure in my ears and at the back of my eyes was terrible. I felt like my eyeballs were going to burst. It was the worst feeling I've ever had on a plane. Maybe it was just where I was sitting, because no one else was affected!'

Suzanne: 'We usually travel light. There's no entourage of make-up people or stylists. I think we're all pretty organized and independent. We just had Tracy Watts from Polydor with us, and our tour manager, Jamal, which is all we need. We're from normal backgrounds and none of us have been mollycoddled, which is good because it means when we go anywhere we just get on with it.'

Hanging around as usual!

Noel: 'When we got to Leipzig we were met by some Polydor people and taken to the hotel. We didn't get a chance to explore because there just wasn't time, but from what we could see, Leipzig is a pretty place. There were trams and some lovely old buildings. And it was so peaceful. We arrived late afternoon, which you'd think would be rush hour, but there was hardly any traffic. It was a lovely sunny day as well and we all wished we had our shorts on. The weather in London before we left had been grim.'

Suzanne: 'We got to the hotel and went straight into an interview on camera for a German website called Bravo. It's good meeting journalists from other countries because you find out all kinds of things you didn't know. The man from Bravo told us that when they did the German *Popstars* show they took the final thirty to Majorca – we only got as far as Brixton! He also wanted to know if there was any truth in the rumour that we've been banned from wearing bikinis.'

We went straight into an interview when we arrived in Germany.

Noel: 'I think he was quite shocked by some of the stories in the British press. The thing is, if you started believing your bad press you'd never get out of bed in the

We finally arrive.

morning, and if you believed all the good things you'd end up with a big head. But it seems like the press in Germany is very different to the UK.'

Danny: 'We'd only been in Germany for a couple of hours when I began to get an idea of how big the show was that we'd be doing the next day. I found out that people like Shaggy and Westlife were on the bill and I thought, "This is huge." It was a bit like Party in the Park – same sort of scale – only staged indoors.'

Noel: 'Danny started telling us that *The Dome* was a huge show. None of us had realized. Maybe if we had, we would have brought a stylist after all ...'

Myleene: 'We had no idea how big it was, then an interviewer asked me if we were going to be wearing spectacular outfits. We were in our jeans! I told her that the song we were performing was called Pure And Simple and that just about summed up our outfits too! It didn't matter to me because I'd always much rather see a performer singing their heart out than fussing over their outfit.'

Kym: 'We'd just taken our jeans and casual stuff because we genuinely didn't know what *The Dome* was. It turned out to be a bit like the Brits, in a massive venue and with an audience of millions. We were all very relaxed about it because it wasn't until we actually arrived for rehearsals the next day that we got an idea of the scale of the event.'

5.0

TIME CHECK

The first single that Danny bought was by Kylie Minogue; they're both May babies – Kylie in 1968 and Danny in 1979.

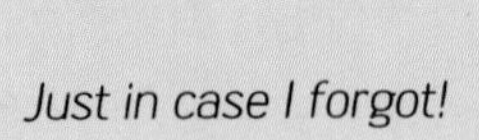

Just in case I forgot!

Suzanne: 'On the day of the show we had our make-up done before leaving the hotel, then travelled ninety kilometres by road to Riesa for the show. On the way we heard on the radio that there were traffic jams because so many people were trying to get there. *The Dome* goes out four times a year in Germany. It's live and always comes from a different location – and it draws the biggest audience of any music show there.

'As soon as we got there we went on stage to rehearse – and saw the size of the venue. It was huge, with two giant video screens and a massive glitter ball hanging from the ceiling. We ran through "Pure And Simple" while they did lighting and sound checks, then as soon as we came off we did an interview before going back to the dressing room. You think you're going to have hours to kill before the show goes live but we did a lot of interviews and photos. We also filmed something with No Angels, who seemed really together. In no time at all we were getting changed and having hair and make-up checks, ready for the show.'

Danny: 'We did a few interviews and everyone wanted to know more or less the same things – how we'd found the *Popstars* experience and whether the plan had been to have a mixed band from the outset. They're all interested in that because most of the other *Popstars* bands have been all girls. Someone asked Myleene for the good and bad points of having guys in the band. She said, "The best thing is their voices give you more depth, and the worst thing is they smell!"'

Myleene: 'We did an interview with Bravo TV, which was really good fun, and they asked us if there was any prospect of teaming up with No Angels on a track. Noel said, "We've only just met them today but I'd like to see more of them." I said, "I bet you would – over dinner and a bottle of champagne!"'

Danny: 'I thought No Angels were well together. The thing about *Popstars* is we've all gone through the same thing and we can relate to that, but really that's all we do share. All the *Popstars* groups are totally different, they all have their own style, and you can't compare them.'

Myleene: 'There was a lot going on behind the scenes and loads of people everywhere, but they'd really got it together on the catering front – the food was fantastic! I'd been feeling poorly the day before with a chest cold. I knew I wasn't well because I went to bed early without eating, which is unheard of for me – I love

Another day, another interview!

The food at The Dome *was brilliant!*

my food. I knew I was feeling fine again when I discovered rhubarb purée and rhubarb yoghurt on the pudding menu ... delicious!'

Kym: 'There was so much going on during the day – camera crews roaming around the whole time and lots of different interviews. Apart from No Angels, we didn't know who the German artists were. There was one amazing-looking girl with a huge mane of blonde hair and very elaborate make-up. She was really turning heads and we were all dying to know who she was. It turned out she wasn't a performer at all – she was a make-up artist!'

Suzanne: 'Our dressing room always looks a bit chaotic just because there's five of us so it gets crowded. Usually there's only one mirror, which means everyone's crowding round at the same time. In Germany, we had someone doing hair and make-up, so it was a bit of a squeeze. Danny's got the right attitude. He just sat in a corner with his headphones on, listening to Destiny's Child!'

Noel's autograph joins a host of others on the famous Dome *poster.*

TIME CHECK

Myleene is a Harry Potter *fan. Just a week after* The Way to Your Love *shot to number one,* Harry Potter and The Goblet of Fire *became the UK's bestselling book.*

With No Angels, the winners of the German Popstars.

Noel: 'You spend all day building up to a performance then you go on and a few minutes later it's all over. It was a brilliant experience and the audience reacted well to us. We were invited to a big after-show party, which we'd have loved to go to, but we had an early flight back to London the next day so we had to get back to the hotel. An hour after coming off stage we were packed and on our way back to Leipzig – singing pub songs all the way!'

Kym: 'It's important to us to break Hear'say in Europe. We want to maintain our support in the UK and make a name for ourselves elsewhere. We know it's going to be difficult. You can't just rush in and out of a place in five seconds flat and expect that to be enough, so we're prepared to work at it.'

Danny: 'It's good for us to go to Europe. It's a grounding and to some extent a sobering experience because no one knows who you are. You've had a huge hit with

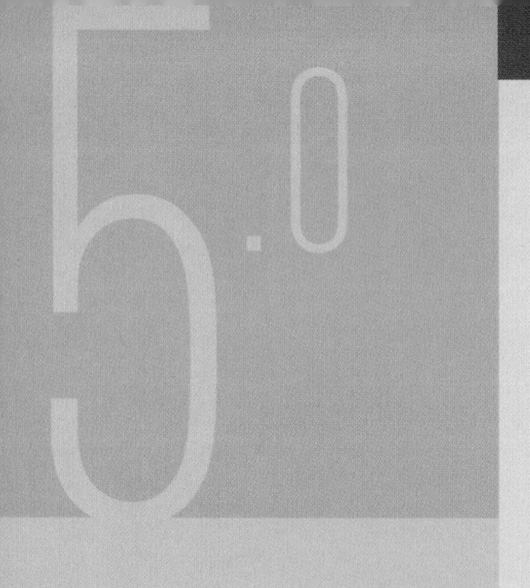

"Pure And Simple" in the UK but it's a new market in Europe and that's good for you. You walk down the street and no one knows you, and it's a reminder that not everyone knows who Hear'say is. It also reminds you that nothing can be taken for granted and that you have to work every territory. The other thing is you get your naivety back. *The Dome* is a huge show but we'd never heard of it, never seen it. It makes you realize how much you still have to learn. If we break Europe that will be great.'

Kym: 'The day after we got back from Germany we were moving out of the *Popstars* house, and we had to decide how to divide everything up so we did a lucky dip on the plane on the way home. We wrote all the contents of the house onto bits of paper and put them in a sick-bag and drew lots. Suzy came off worst – she ended up with a table and chairs, a lamp, a humidifier, some books and plates – things she didn't want. I was lucky – I got the fridge-freezer and the DVD. The boys got the computer, so they were well pleased, and Noel demanded the Welsh edition of Monopoly! Myleene ended up with the one household appliance she is hopeless with – the washing machine!'

One last photograph before we go home.

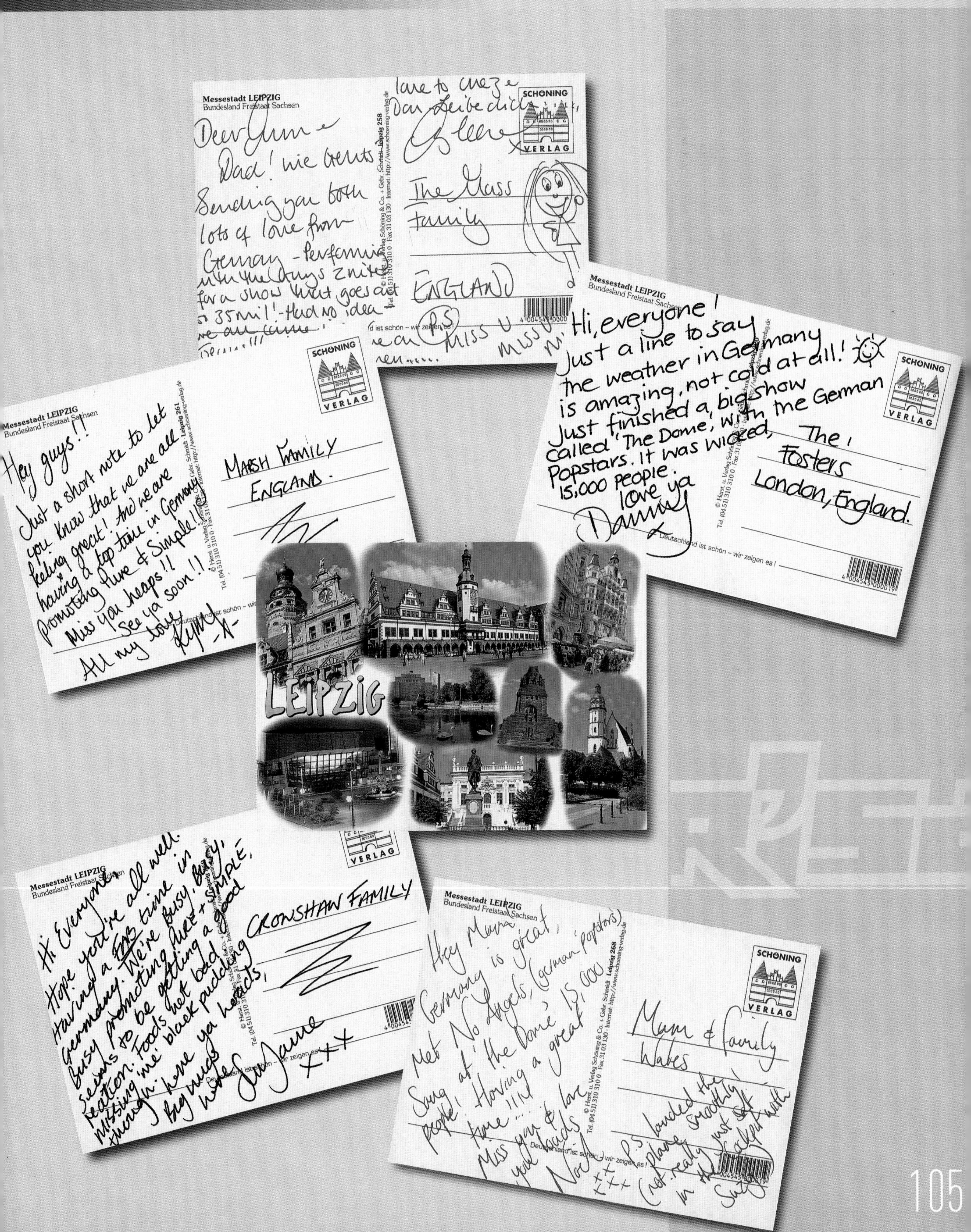

Messestadt LEIPZIG
Bundesland Freistaat Sachsen

Dear Mum + Dad! Wie Gehts?
Sending you both lots of love from Germany - Performing with the boys 2nite for a show that goes out to 35mil! - Had no idea we all came ... Germany!!!

love to Chezi
Dan Liebe dich
Glee x

The Glass Family
ENGLAND

P.S. MISS U

Messestadt LEIPZIG
Bundesland Freistaat Sachsen

Hey guys!!
Just a short note to let you know that we are all feeling great! And we are having a top time in Germany promoting Pure & Simple!!
Miss you heaps!!
See ya soon!!
All my love
Kym -X-

MARSH FAMILY
ENGLAND.

Messestadt LEIPZIG
Bundesland Freistaat Sachsen

Hi, everyone!
Just a line to say the weather in Germany is amazing, not cold at all! Just finished a big show called 'The Dome', with the German Popstars. It was wicked, 15,000 people.
love ya
Danny x

The Fosters
London, England.

Deutschland ist schön – wir zeigen es!

LEIPZIG

Messestadt LEIPZIG
Bundesland Freistaat Sachsen

Hi Everyone,
Hope you're all well. Having a FAB time in Germany. We're busy, busy, busy promoting Pure + Simple. Seems to be getting a good reaction. Food's not bad, missing me black pudding though.
Love ya heaps,
Big hugs
Suzanne xxx

CRONSHAW FAMILY

Messestadt LEIPZIG
Bundesland Freistaat Sachsen

Hey Mam,
Germany is great, met No Angels (German 'popstars') Sang at 'the Dome' 15,000 people! Having a great time!!!!
Miss you & love you loads
Noel xxx

P.S. landed the plane smoothly (not really just sat in the cockpit with Suz)

Mum & family
Wales

SCHÖNING VERLAG

MOVING OUT... MOVING ON

6

Myleene: 'I had this idea that we'd shut the door together with some kind of fanfare to mark us leaving the *Popstars* house. I felt it would be the end of one era and the beginning of another, but that isn't how it happened at all. We left in dribs and drabs. It was a sad ending to a wicked time.'

Kym washing up in our new kitchen. As we got busier, we didn't have time to do any housework at all.

Myleene: 'The *Popstars* house used to stand for so much to me. It's where we all met and spent so much time together. It was always filled with music and laughter. I was apprehensive about moving out because I knew I was going to miss everybody.'

Danny: 'We did spend a lot of time in the house. We had time to sit round and talk, play board games, order in pizza and stuff – that was our bonding time.'

Kym: 'I don't think we felt we wanted to move but we knew it was imminent. We didn't really want to leave each other but we knew the time had come.'

Noel: 'In some ways moving out of the *Popstars* house was scary because there was this sense of "Where are we going to go?" I felt really safe in that house with the others but when the time came to leave I think we were glad to be going. The house was stinking because we were working eighteen-hour days and five people living in one place is a big mess anyway. Towards the end fans were turning up, which was fine, but there was non-stop knocking on the door and calling through the letterbox and stuff. On the day we moved out I had a 'mare. I really lost the plot because I couldn't get my stuff packed. Everyone was rushing round telling me to hurry up and in the end I just went, "*No.*" I ended up staying at the house with Myleene and doing it in my own time.

'I think moving out felt like moving away from home for the first time because the house was an abnormal situation really, a bit like a holiday camp. It's only now I feel I've flown the nest properly. I miss the atmosphere and it's weird seeing everyone go off to their separate places, but it's good for us as well to have our own space. I did think it might change our relationship but we all still spend a massive amount of the day together and the basis of what is Hear'say is very strong.'

TIME CHECK

Kym was just eight when one of her favourite soaps – EastEnders *– was first screened.*

Myleene: 'On the day they were all moving I was going to be the only one left behind because my flat wasn't ready. I didn't want to see them packing and walking out the door – that felt too symbolic – so I went round to my mum and dad's. Then I got a phone call from Noel and he was quite upset. He just couldn't do it. I said it was fine, I'd help him move the next day, I went to the house and we just hung out together. Everyone else had gone. I understood exactly how he felt. There's a time for these things and it was a big step. I think he felt very alone. I take it for granted that I live in London and my family is here. If my family was in Wales they would seem a million miles away, and that's how he feels. It's the same for Kym and Suzy. Danny and I are the home birds and that makes it easier for us.'

Noel: 'I think Danny and Myleene take it for granted they can go home and spend time with their families. It's a five-hour trip for me to get back to Cardiff. It's just something you have to get on with, but some days I feel down. I don't see my family and friends as much as I'd like and that's really tough. Some days I get narky and people don't know why, but that's it – it's just that I miss people.'

Danny: 'I couldn't wait to get out of the Mill Hill house. It didn't belong to us and there was a deadline to leave. I'll be honest – I had to go. It was really filthy because

The house was lovely when we moved in.

6.0

Danny, Kym and Myleene scour the papers.

we never had a chance to clean, we had a smashed window at the back, and fans were turning up there, which was nice but it started to get a bit malicious. People were throwing stones at the windows and camping out in the back garden to listen in on our conversations – these were adults, girls in their twenties.

'All these things just brought a bad karma to the house. We got to the point where we dreaded going back there. There were clothes everywhere, the washing never got done. Me and Noel hardly ever washed our sheets. It was ironic. We were Hear'say and people probably thought we were living the life of Riley but the truth was we had milk with mould in it, which stunk the place out. It was just an unhealthy place to be.

'I do believe it was time to separate, but I also think we could easily have found a big house and all still be living together now. It's wicked to be in a band together but I don't think you can share everything. We were watching the same films, eating the same food, talking about the same things. We never got bored but now it's great because we go our separate ways and then we have different things to talk about when we're all together. We have more freedom in a way. Suzy's thinking of getting a dog and she couldn't have done that at Mill Hill because she'd have had to ask the four of us. Now she can do what she wants.'

Suzanne: 'The *Popstars* house at Mill Hill is such a big memory for us. I like to think about it in the early days, when it was clean and tidy and we used to go shopping and split the chores between us. It got to the point where we were just too busy. In the end the house really wasn't clean. It was unhygienic. We had so many people coming and going there. We had a false fridge in the kitchen and someone had put milk in there and forgotten to remove it. We didn't know what the smell was, then finally we found the milk, but by then we couldn't get rid of the stench. I used to walk in and feel sick. Because we were never there it got really messy too.

'On the day we moved it wasn't like we suddenly left each other because it happened in stages. Kym was the first to go, then me, then the lads, then Myleene. It's not like we don't see each other. We're together a lot. We visit each other's new places.'

Myleene: 'Once everyone had moved it was so sad. The house felt so lonely. It made me realize a home isn't just bricks and mortar – it's the people who live there. I half expected to see Kym walking round in her Superman pyjamas or Suzy wandering out of the bathroom in her dressing-gown, or Noel and Danny fighting and pushing the mattress over the banister for the umpteenth time, or Danny playing Anastacia full blast. When they weren't there it just felt really strange.

'I only stayed there one night on my own. It wasn't the same at all. Then we had three burglaries in the space of a few days. The first time it was just kids, messing round, and they took memorabilia. I was upset because one of the things that was taken was a gift Suzy had brought me back from her holiday. It was a plaque with "Marlene" on it – people are always getting my name wrong and calling me Marlene – so that had sentimental value.

'The second burglary was worse. I walked in and everything was all over the floor. The police told me that doesn't often happen, but whoever did it knew the place was empty and they took their time. They went through everything. I was so upset. They took my camera, which had photos of the band on the film, they took videos, CDs, things that were really personal to me. They took my DVD player and that was precious because it was a gift from Polydor when "Pure And Simple" went to number one. I'm just glad no one was in the house and that nobody was hurt. Noel and me locked up and boarded up a window that had been smashed. There was a hex sign on the lawn at the back, which seemed vindictive.

'I didn't want to go back again but there were still things I needed, so I went back once more with Noel and we discovered there had been another break-in. I realized it was never going to stop and I just had to go for good. In the early days living there, I had this idea that we'd all shut the door together with some kind of fanfare to mark us leaving the *Popstars* house. I felt it would be the end of one era and the beginning of another, but that isn't how it happened at all. We left in dribs and drabs. It was a sad ending to a wicked time.

'When I finally shut the door I felt relief because I knew someone had been through

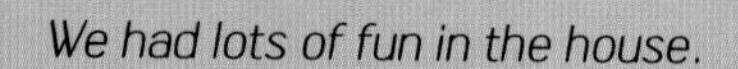

We had lots of fun in the house.

my underwear, my clothes, all my personal things. The only time I've had to work through my tears was after the burglaries. The big one happened just before a photo shoot and I was crying in between the pictures being taken.'

Noel: 'I think me and Danny decided to share a place because we'd shared a room in the *Popstars* house and we just got on really well. We'd sit up all night talking. We wanted to be in Hackney, rather than anywhere pop-starry, like Hampstead. We've got a great flat but it's very bare at the moment. It has wooden floors, white walls and massive windows. It's really modern and light – a proper lads' pad.'

Very funny Noel!

Danny: 'You'd think we'd want our own space after sharing at Mill Hill but we didn't feel like that. We love our new place but we need to make it a bit more homely. In the living room we've got a widescreen TV, a Playstation 2, a dining table and chairs, and some cushions. We also bought a microwave and an iron – can you believe it? I can iron! Everyone told me to get a decent iron so I spent £65 on one. It's lucky I did because the other day we went to Southampton and I didn't find out until this morning – three days later – that Noel had left the iron on all that time. Luckily, it's got an automatic cut-off, otherwise the place would have probably burned down.

'We get on really well. There's just one tiny thing: I hate it when people blank you and go off into a world of their own, and Noel does that quite a bit. It really annoys me! Apparently Claire, his mum, does it as well, so that's probably where he gets it. I don't think I've got too many quirks, except I hate feet! I can't stand them – they're horrible. They should be hidden under socks and shoes at all times.'

Suzanne: 'One night I was in my new flat on my own and I just felt so proud. I'm in a nice flat, I've got a comfortable life, and that's a good feeling. I've totally adapted to living in London. I feel this is my home now, I love it so much. I'm close to Hampstead, which is like a village, with lots of shops and bars. It's great.

'I love my flat. The front room is really big. There are patio doors leading to the garden, which is full of trees and really private. My bedroom's got patio doors onto the garden and an *en suite* bathroom. I'm sharing with Andrea, a friend from home, and her room is next to mine. She also has her own bathroom. She's a brilliant flatmate. The style of the place is very modern with lots of light wood. And no sour milk in the fridge!'

Myleene: 'I haven't got a scrap of furniture in my house apart from my bed, but I don't care! The first night I didn't even have any sheets. I borrowed Suzy's duvet, but the feeling of lying in a bed I'd bought myself in my flat made me feel I'd achieved something. My mum and dad came round and I couldn't even give them a cup of tea because I didn't have a kettle or any mugs, so I gave them lemonade and they drank out of wineglasses. I've got one completely empty room but I love walking round it thinking, "This is mine" – and I'm really proud of that.'

Kym: 'My new place is very nice, very secure, but I'm only going to be here for six months. It's a one-bedroom flat, very bright and spacious, and lets in lots of natural light. It's got cream carpets and I'm just going to keep the colours very simple – blues and blacks. The bedroom is lilac and cream. There's a gym in the building, which is great, so I can train. The best thing is, you know how everyone's house has a smell? Well, this one has a nice smell. It's comforting and welcoming.'

Myleene: 'I miss living with them. I miss being with them, and their laughter. But the good thing is that now we have new things to tell each other. The joke is we're always round at each other's places anyway.'

Kym: 'I *am* happy in London and I do know my way round a bit now, but I would be happier in the north because that's where I'm from – it sums me up and I miss it. I just want to walk down the street and say, "Morning!" If you do that here people think you want to stab them in the neck or something, and I don't know why that is. In general, people in London find it hard to believe you're just being friendly. In the north, anything goes. I'd like it a lot better in London if my children were with me and my family was around because we're very close. Every time I leave there are tears and it doesn't get any easier.'

Suzanne: 'I don't think we'll drift apart, but it's good for us to have our own space. I enjoy being with my flatmate. She's not part of my work and we can talk about different things. The five of us will always be strong but we need other relationships in our lives.'

In the early days we had time to muck about and hang out.

Kym and Jack: 'We're good friends as well as everything else.'

Kym: 'I was on my own for a while, then I met Jack (Ryder) and I'm really happy. We're moving in together for six months in October. I'm moving out of my flat because kids have found out where I live and they call up to the window, "Kym – Jack!" So I think the best thing to do is to move. Jack suggested I move in with him and the more I thought about it the more it made sense. We're both really excited about it – we're like little kids. We talk about it and go *aaaarghhh!* It's going to be really good. I'm planning to buy a house next year but this could be a trial run for the future. Jack's never lived with anyone before but we get on really well. We see each other most nights anyway and we've got to know each other so well in such a short space of time that I don't think it will mean extra pressure on us. If I'm not at his, he's at mine. People say I'll get a chance to find out what his bad habits are but I already know – he has plenty! But he's Jack and I love him.

'We met for the first time at Elstree Studios. We were doing *Top of the Pops* and he'd been doing *EastEnders*. I'd gone into the bar with Mark Lamarr and the band, and Jack was there. It was just, "Oh hi, I'm Jack," and we chatted. I thought it was nice that he introduced himself. When I left, I went rushing about screaming, "I've just met Jack Ryder!" It was really funny. I was running up the corridor knocking on all the dressing-room doors, telling everyone I'd been talking to Jack. They were all laughing at me because I was in a dither. Eventually, I calmed down a bit.

'Then we met up a few times just by coincidence. I was in Red Cube, a club in London, one night with Suzy and he was there. Then we went out to Spain to shoot the video for our second single and he was there at the same time, which was very strange. There were all these weird coincidences going on and it just seemed like someone was trying to tell us something. We kept being thrown together and I was thinking that, actually, I quite fancied him. He was also thinking he quite fancied me and we just decided to give it a shot, and now to me he's just Jack.

'I'm a big believer in fate and when you feel you're being thrown together you just think, "Okay, let's just see what happens." It didn't take long for us to realize we were getting on well – we knew after about a week. We are very similar and have so much in common. He doesn't believe all the hype and neither do I. So many people think they're better than everyone else because they've had some success, but that's not what we're about.

'We didn't really have a first date. We couldn't go out anywhere because people would have seen us and started talking, so I just went round to his house. You never know what's going to happen, if things are going to work out. So we stayed out of the public eye and saw each other in secret for a while. Then we realized we had feelings for each other and that it was going to work, and we decided to do things the right way. It was so funny in the meantime. The press were trying to get pictures of us and we wouldn't let them. I took him to Wigan to meet my family and my kids, and on the way back on the train we got a tip-off that there were photographers waiting for us at the station in London. So he went to one end of the train and I went to the other, and we got off separately. We wanted to save it for the Soap Awards and that was a big relief. Now we can walk down the street together and it's fine.

'He is very honest and straight to the point, very direct and genuine, loyal and loving. He's romantic and takes me out for meals. He gets on so well with my children – he loves them. He's very private, down-to-earth and just a normal guy. He's also very cute! I keep thinking he's too perfect, that there's bound to be something bad waiting to come out, but I haven't found it. I think he's like me – what you see is what you get. I think he's too honest to be hiding something. He's got one of those see-through faces – you'd be able to tell if he was lying about something and I don't think he would anyway. I've only known him a short time but I think I know him well.

'The only thing I hate is that he can eat whatever he wants and he doesn't seem to put any weight on! He is skinny. Another thing is he never ever looks ugly, not ever. He always looks lovely. He looks great in the morning when he wakes up. That's one of the best times. He just looks amazing. It's very hard to keep my hands off him! I don't see him as a sex symbol, although that's how I thought of him before I met him. He clearly doesn't feel he deserves the sex symbol thing. He actually hates fame. He is such a talented person. He's an amazing guitarist and he can sing, although he won't admit to that. I love hearing him play and sing.

'I was advised that it would be difficult if I got involved with him because we're both in the public eye and also because of the age difference – he's nineteen and I'm twenty-five – but I was prepared for that. Jack actually has an older head on his shoulders, and that's probably because he was involved in *EastEnders* from a young

TIME CHECK

Kym's boyfriend, Jack Ryder, first appeared in EastEnders *on 9 November 1998.*

Noel sorts out his rubbish.

age. I just thought, "I'm a girl and he's a guy and that's it, end of story." I'm not going to let newspapers dictate who I can and can't see. I will never let them rule my life. I never did before and I'm not now. I think you have to be strong. If you just roll over, you're in trouble. I thought I'd get hate mail from girls but I haven't had any. So far everyone has been nice and there's no bad feeling from fans. I've met the *EastEnders* cast and his friends there and they're really nice people, but he's also got a lot of mates that are just normal everyday folk. I've met his mum and his step-dad and they're really nice, but I was so scared about that. I don't like meeting mums because I know what I'd be like. You always want to impress and you're always a bit scared that you're not going to. We met at his house, then went for dinner. I was just myself and we got on. She came to my birthday party. I haven't met his dad yet because every time we make arrangements I end up working, but I'm looking forward to that. His dad was lead singer in a band called Wang Chung, so we should get on.

'I don't see how I could have a relationship with someone who isn't known now. I don't know how I could trust them. In the back of my mind I'd always be wondering if they were with me because I have money, because of who I am or what I do. There would always be that doubt in your head. I think the only way I can be happy is to be with someone who does their own thing, who has a busy life and understands what my job is about, and who knows I can't be there all the time. We've got a tour coming up and I'm going to be away for about three months, and he's prepared for that.

'At the moment Jack is definitely the one. We have something special. I don't think I've ever felt so much so quickly for someone. I think we're good friends as well as everything else, and that counts for something. We were friends first and the fact we're now seeing each other just makes things better.

'Despite what's happened in the past I still have the dream of what I want my relationship to be – I want to get married, maybe have more children, set up a home. I just want to be happy. I look at my mum and dad and they struggled, but they love each other every bit as much now as they did when they got married more than thirty years ago. They are devoted to each other and that's what I want out of a relationship. I don't want anything less. I think when you've been brought up in that kind of environment it rubs off on you. I'm a hopeless romantic.

'I don't know if you see things differently when you come from a one-parent family because you've maybe seen break-ups and rows – I know a lot of people from that background are cautious about marriage. But for me it's a big deal and not to be taken lightly. I won't marry someone until I know he's the one, which is why I didn't marry the other two people I was with. I knew I wasn't going to be with them for ever and I don't want to have three or four marriages behind me.

'I want to marry once and only once and be happy. I don't want to put up with something because I thought it was what I wanted. I want to enter marriage knowing what I'm doing and that I'm with the person I want to be with for life. I always said I wouldn't get married, but I will – just not yet. I've got loads I want to do first. I've talked to Jack about marriage. I think if you're really in love with someone you do talk about it, but we've only been seeing each other for a few months so it will be a while before anything like that happens. He is the most faithful person ever. I trust him

Working eighteen-hour days meant housework just didn't get done.

Kym packs up her stuff.

completely. He is so loyal, not the sort of person to let you down. He would never cheat on me. He hates two-timing with a passion.'

Danny: 'Things change in lots of ways when you have this kind of experience. My life isn't the same and my relationship with Chloe, my girlfriend, has changed too. I'd known Chloe for a while before we started seeing each other – our families knew each other. We'd have been together four years by now. I'm only twenty-two and that's a long time to be in a relationship at this age. Before *Popstars* we saw each other every day, we did the same things, and the relationship was fantastic, but it's no longer what it used to be.

'Chloe's doing a degree, working really hard, doing her exams. She's doing what she wants to do and I'm in the band. No one would ever have imagined that Hear'say would be so big or that it would take up so much of my time. It means we don't see each other every day, and the only way to keep in contact is on the phone. Phone relationships are very hard because a lot of things get muddled up. Then you end up having a text relationship and you need more than that.

'What happened with me and Chloe is we have kind of split, but I don't feel it's a total split. I can't describe it in any other way. All I can say is we don't see each other as often as we did but when we get the opportunity – which is once in a blue moon – we do. The other Sunday I went down to Canterbury, had a meal and a few drinks, came back the next day, and we had a really nice time. That's just how it will be now and I think that's typical of a young relationship. We're excellent friends, there's a good foundation there, and we still go on dates, but only when we both have the time to be together. We still have a four-year history behind us.

'You never know, we might have time off and a few years down the line we might get married. Maybe next week Chloe will find someone else, maybe next week I will, but for now I think it's fair for both of us to be clear about things because that way no one gets hurt. Chloe agrees. It was a little tricky to shift the relationship from what it was before, but we were able to sit down and talk about things and it's good we were able to speak. I like that.

'I think out of everyone she deserves a pat on the back because we were in our relationship a long time, then suddenly I went away to do this *Popstars* thing and not once did she ever show a jealous streak. She was always behind me because I was doing what I want to do and that's really cool – that's a nice person. I think there came a time when it was apparent just how much I was working, in the run-up to "Pure And Simple" being released. This job doesn't just entail doing a couple of performances then having a week off and getting your private life back. I think we performed "Pure And Simple" something like sixty times on various TV shows. With the second single she knew what to expect and we were in agreement with each other. The new show, *Hear'say – It's Saturday,* was coming up, and so was the tour.

'When I thought about the next time I'd get to see Chloe it was looking like Christmas. I don't even know what we'll be doing then, but I know we'll be working part of the time. So the next time I'd be able to see Chloe properly would probably be January 2002. How do you do that? Tell someone you'll meet for a drink in 2002? It's not fair. So we talked about things and we're both happy.

'I'm wary of new people and I'm cautious of people in this industry. When I talk to them if they're down-to-earth that's cool, but a lot of people are pretentious and a lot of people want to put us down, so I'm wary of that. I'm also on my guard with new "friends and family" that have appeared on the horizon. If someone from the past calls me I always ask myself if they'd have called before Hear'say. That's a good test. In general it has been fine.

'If I went into another relationship it would have to be thought out really well. I'd really have to get to know the person. It would have to be someone I felt 100 per cent comfortable with. You have to be on your guard because people do sell stories and you're not just looking out for yourself – you're looking out for the band too.'

David and Emily's last night in the Popstars house.

Myleene: 'Keeping a relationship going is difficult because you just don't see each other much – it's so hard to get any time. Any relationship is hard enough without all the extra pressures of being in the public eye.

'I've just split up with my boyfriend, David, When we sat down and called it a day we ended things still saying, "I love you". It didn't end with one of us going off with someone else or anything awful, but there is a lot of pressure in this job. I've worked so hard for this opportunity and the chance to be in this position. I really count my lucky stars. This whole experience is unbelievable, and I never take a single day for

6.0

Myleene and David. 'We've been through so much together.'

granted, but you really must invest the hours of work. You work really long, irregular hours – sometimes eighteen-hour days – come home late and get three or four hours sleep. You might have had the most mad, surreal day of your life, but it's very hard to explain that to someone else. Sometimes you don't even want to talk, you're so exhausted. I never know where I'm going to be from one day to the next, and that's hard enough for me to get my head round, never mind someone else.

'Davey put up with all that, but I don't want people to put up with it. I want people to live it with me and it just got to the stage where I felt he should live his own life without all that baggage. I want him to be happy. It's that whole thing – if you love someone, set them free. You can't leave someone hanging on, it's just not fair to pencil someone in all the time and to fit them into your diary here and there. That's what I have with my manager and I don't want it with someone I love.

'We met three months before the *Popstars* auditions. There was a casting for a movie, *Demon Hunters*, and I really wanted to do it. I'd missed the first two castings because I was in Cyprus, working, but they asked me along a third time. I got to play the part of Oerlin, a woodland elf from another dimension that kills demons and vampires – brilliant! A few days after I got the part, I walked into the casting room and David was there. He's such a good-looking guy but I didn't really say much. Sometimes, you see a good-looking guy and you can't tell whether they're just going to love themselves, so I stayed away. I thought, either he's gay or he's married! Then we got talking and got on like a house on fire. He's a model, but he hates the contrived side of that job, he's not from that kind of background. He's a very grounded person, very funny, and I liked that.

'When we were filming our scenes together, we had a real chemistry between us. But despite that I didn't want anything to happen there and then because I knew that would affect the film. Things could have gone either way and I didn't want them to go the wrong way. On the last night, we went for a drink and a meal, and that was it. We just ended up together. Everyone was really happy for us; he's such a lovely guy, so passionate and so honest with me. He had everything I go for– personality, intelligence, humour – and he loves classical music. Everyone notices how good-looking he is, but I saw beyond that. He was someone I could really talk to, we were happier just sitting round in our pyjamas chatting than going out for fancy meals.

'I didn't think I'd get into the band but he would say, 'Yeah, you're going to get it, I just have a feeling.' He really believed I would. He stuck by me all the way through and when the *Popstars* phenomenon hit, he was a rock for me. It was hard for him because, before *Popstars*, I'd been there all the time, then I was taken away from him and we hardly saw each other. And then suddenly my old love life – photographs with ex-boyfriends – was all over the papers. I can't tell you what it feels like when you pick up the paper and see your love life splashed all over the front page. For a start, it's really not that interesting; people are dying, there are earthquakes, planes crashing – and the story on the front page is about you! And it's not even true.

'David went through absolute hell with people selling stories to the newspapers. He really suffered. He had his car damaged, awful letters sent and awful things said about me, trying to scare him – trying to scare us both. One girl stalked him, and did horrendous things. He obviously wasn't interested in her, and she took it badly and made a lot of money talking to the newspapers. I can't comprehend it; there are some very desperate, very greedy people out there who don't care.

'One paper actually ran a story that said, "If you're one of David's 300 ex-lovers we want to hear from you ... and we'll give you a few grand." That was like opening the floodgates. Every time I went into a radio station or did an interview I was asked about my "love rat" and it was really hard. Somehow we coped, but you can't laugh about it because it's too painful. We've both been victims of opportunists who sell stories to the press. I didn't ever say, "Is it true?" When we first met I said to him, "I really care a lot about you and all I want is complete honesty." So because we'd already had that discussion, we knew where we stood.

'We've been through so much together – he's a huge part of my life. I miss having him to talk to. I miss the hugs, the banter, the whole package. I believe once you find your soul mate you'll always have a connection with that person.

'Now that it's over, I do think "Did I do the right thing?" It's hard because you sacrifice so much in this job. It's a dream job, but there is a price to pay, whether it's not seeing your friends as often as you'd like or reaching the point with your relationship where you feel it's not right to have someone waiting. He's not one of those people who would just follow me round. You hear about girlfriends and boyfriends who go out with someone in this position and they just hang out with them the whole time. They don't get on with their own lives, and that's fine if you're happy with that, but he has his own life.

'I've never had a relationship like the one I had with Davey. Before I went out with him, I was always just "dating", but suddenly I was thinking, "My God, I could spend my life with you" and I've never had that before. I did think I might marry him and you don't know what's in the future. He knew me before Hear'say – he is that connection to my old life. If it's meant to be, it will happen. Whatever the future holds, I'll go with that.

IT'S ALL GO!

7

Kym: 'Performing live and meeting the fans is what we're all about. That's the most important thing. All we want to do is give the best we can every time we go on stage.'

The stylist trims Kym's sleeve – no detail goes unnoticed! Meanwhile, Danny relaxes with a magazine.

Kym: 'We were told we'd be shooting the video for the second single, "The Way To Your Love", in Spain and we thought, "Amazing". We thought it would be so great to go somewhere hot because with "Pure And Simple" we shot the video in a laser testing site in Southend, in Essex, and it was cold and filthy. We were imagining sun and sangria and it *was* beautiful for the first couple of days. We did the photo shoot for the cover of the single and had some time off, and the weather was nice and bright.'

Myleene: 'We had a wonderful time playing in the pool in Marbella, then we went to the plains of Granada for the video shoot and the weather was horrendous. We were up at 5 a.m. and we thought it would clear up but it just got worse. Everyone was ready to start; they'd built this amazing stage and we all wanted it to be great.'

Danny: "The weather was nice to begin with and we had a day off, so we went in the pool and had a couple of beers, and got snapped by some paparazzi who were hiding in the bushes. It was my birthday on the day of the shoot and I was first on set at 5.30 a.m. Me and Noel filmed in the morning and it was fairly sunny, but the weather got worse during the day. It started to rain and by the time the girls had to do their bit it was cold and raining hard.'

Kym: 'We'd arrived at Granada at night so we didn't really know what the weather was like, but the next day it was absolutely heaving down. It was freezing – there was snow in Myleene's hair. We were all in little strappy tops and peep-toe sandals. Suzy's toes were so cold she was screaming with pain, but we just had to carry on.'

Suzanne: 'We wanted it to be a phenomenal video and it was turning into a disaster. It started to hail and it even snowed. I did get to the point where I thought I had frostbite in my feet and was in tears. There were moments when it was so awful we just laughed. I was just thinking, "Please let's get this over with."'

TIME CHECK

Suzanne's favourite TV programme is Friends. Series One started in 1994, when Suzanne was just 13.

Danny: '*cdUK* were filming behind the scenes, which was good because it showed that video shoots aren't as glamorous as people think. It's not all sun-kissed beaches and you sing a couple of lines then sunbathe for the rest of the day...'

Myleene: 'A lot of time and money and effort had gone into the video and we all wanted it to be great, so we were prepared to put 100 per cent effort in. As the weather got worse, we felt we just had to be strong and get it finished. I had a basque on and I have never been so cold in my life. Suzy's feet had turned blue. To add to the misery, there was a helicopter overhead doing aerial shots and that was whipping up a wind and making it feel even colder.'

Suzanne: 'We kept going for two days and we thought we'd got it, but when we looked at the video you could see we were suffering. It was disastrous.'

Kym: 'We got through it then we heard the video was rubbish and we would have to re-shoot.'

Myleene: 'We watched it and all I could see was the pain on our faces and the rainclouds in the sky.'

What about this one? Suzanne doesn't look convinced, while Noel lounges about, unconcerned. What is it about boys?

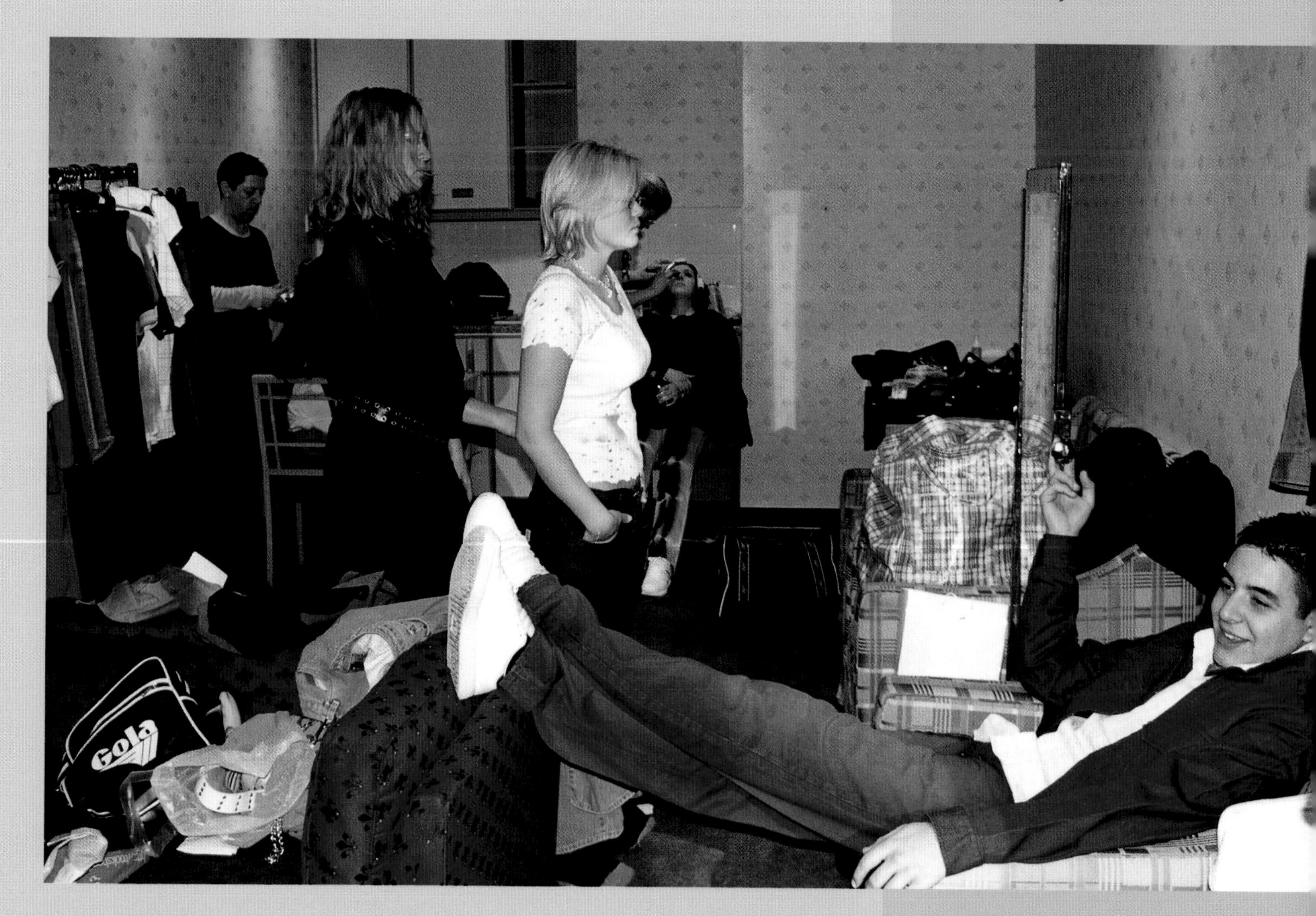

7.0

(right and facing page) Make-up is finished, clothes are sorted, at last we can get down to filming the video!

Danny: 'Everyone was saying the video was terrible. I was the only one going, "It's wicked!" I thought it looked really cool but that's me – optimistic Danny.'

Noel: 'It was a bit of a scramble to re-shoot the video. We came back from Germany and had a day and a half to learn a new routine, then a day to shoot a new video. We weren't taking any chances with the weather this time so we went to a big sound stage at Asylum Studios in north London. The crew had just a day to build the set and they did an amazing job. It really looked like a dusty, hot location. The art director, Andy Radford, worked round the clock to design and build it. There were "mountains" made of roofing felt covered in sand and gravel and plants. The boulders were made of polystyrene. They looked real but they weighed hardly anything. The crew brought in sixty bags of sand to make the floor look like the desert. There is so much work in these things. It's an amazing illusion.'

Danny: 'On the day of the re-shoot we were at the studio by 7 a.m. We had a big area to ourselves with a make-up room and a wardrobe area with all the different outfits set out on rails. If you weren't needed on set you could chill out, so it was a great location. Making a video is a painstaking process – it has to be. You're miming to playback and you do it line by line. You have to do each line over and over because it has to be perfect. It's weird because even the most simple thing like getting up and walking a few steps starts to feel strange when you're doing it again and again.'

Myleene: 'You spend a long time in make-up for a shoot like this. It has to be right and it takes hours. Kym and I seemed to spend the whole day having our hair and make-up done. We weren't needed for something like eight hours and we still had a bit of a panic when we were called. The thing is, you can't get dressed until the last minute in case you crease the clothes or spill something on them, so you're sitting round in your jeans, then suddenly the director wants you on set and it's like, "We're not ready!" I was wearing a corset, which had to be laced up, and it took for ever. I think they were all tearing their hair out!'

Kym: 'I loved my outfit – a tight denim top that had been customized, and a long skirt. I was really comfortable in it. You have to look your best for a pop video because people are going to play it over and over. Sometimes I can't believe how long it takes to get ready, but you have your make-up done, then hours go by and you need to have it retouched before you finally go on set. Myleene and I were called late in the day so we'd had a lot of hanging around and we couldn't get ready until the last minute. I needed some body make-up and I also had to shave under my arms. They were jumping up and down a bit on the set, but there's no point in going on camera unless you look right.'

Danny: 'We had to knuckle down and get the shoot finished in a day because the video had to be out to people like MTV and The Box that week. Sometimes you look at the schedule and think there aren't enough hours in the day, but you get through somehow.'

Noel: 'You're always trying to fit other things in, like signing pictures or album

7.0

sleeves. The record company brought in the photographs from the shoot we'd done in Spain and we went through them to find something for the single cover. Everyone liked different shots – except Danny, who thought they were all wicked! I liked most of them except one batch that made us look like a dodgy cabaret band! In the end there was a pile everyone liked and that's how we picked the cover shot. There were some brilliant shots. We all look so happy.'

Just a little retouch for Danny.

Myleene: 'I got wet first time round in Spain shooting the video, and on the re-shoot at the end of the day we did a shot of me washing my hair and Noel tipped a bucket of water over me. I just thought, "Am I ever going to get through this song without a soaking?!"'

Suzanne: 'I really liked the video we ended up with because we all look like we're having a good time. There's a scene where we're all messing round on the veranda of this little house and it just sort of captures how things are between us.'

Myleene: 'The Way To Your Love is very different to Pure And Simple. I think it's an even stronger song – the vocals are stronger, and it's a harder song to sing. It's one of the songs we did at Stargate in Norway and it was the first time we'd really heard ourselves. The vocals were amazing. You'd think with five voices it would become a battle, but it works. I really love the song.'

Danny: 'It might sound a bit pants to say it, but The Way To Your Love was one of the songs we did in the beginning that really bonded us vocally. We all sat there in the studio at Stargate and supported each other through it all. We were all so new to everything then. I just remember you'd watch everyone do their bit, make their mistakes, and there would be so much encouragement. That definitely shows within the track. When we first heard it back it was like, "This is the one."'

Myleene: 'It just gelled so well. What amazed me was that when we walked into the studio none of us really knew each other's potential. We all knew we could sing but we didn't know how the five voices would come together – I think we're still learning every day. But I remember my reaction when I heard the others. I just thought, "My God, any one of these vocals would be strong enough but to have five together!" It

Suzanne and Noel share a joke with Paul Domaine, the choreographer.

The crew built this amazing set in just one day!

was such a catchy song. I was so excited when I heard it played back.'

Danny: 'For me, the song represents what Hear'say is all about. When we first started as a band, people were saying there had to be a lead vocalist, but we always knew that wasn't the case. We've said a million times we were picked because we are five vocalists. The Way To Your Love proves you *can* have five voices together – everyone's got a part, we're harmonizing. There's the proof it can be done. When it went to number one that was so good for us.'

Myleene: 'People thought it wasn't possible to have five voices, that it would just be too confusing. We knew we could do it and we made it work. It all comes together in the choruses and that's so exciting for us.'

Danny: 'It is a very hard song to sing – a lot tougher than Pure And Simple. When you listen to the track you can hear Noel does some really high ad-libs and they were not contrived in any way. They just came out in the studio.'

Myleene: 'We wanted to release The Way To Your Love as the first single but were advised against it. Pure and Simple is like an anthem – it's great to sing along to and that's what people were waiting for at the end of the series. With the second single we knew we would have to withstand much tougher critical attention and there was

7.0

We had the most amazing time in Newcastle, (Right and facing page) Myleene waves to some people who pulled alongside the pier in their boat.

We didn't want Noel to feel like the odd one out.

no programme to give us an extra push. It was nerve-racking in the weeks leading up to the release, wondering how well it would do. We knew the song was on the album, and 600,000 people had already bought that, so would they buy the single? Even though it was a re-mix and had a great, B-side you never know.'

Danny: 'We knew the second single would be the test of whether we were on the right lines or not in terms of us and our music. People knew us from *Popstars* but this was about lasting beyond the life of the series.'

Myleene: 'We felt edgy all week once it was released. We'd done all the promotion, all the TV appearances, and it was just a matter of waiting. With Pure And Simple we were kept in the dark until the day the chart was announced, but with this one we knew every single day how it was doing.'

Danny: 'To have a second number one is fantastic, but we would have been happy with any chart position. To get into the Top 10 would have been amazing in itself.'

Myleene: 'I don't think you can judge what makes a great song purely on the basis of record sales. There are some classic songs that have barely made it into the Top 10 – it depends what the market's like. We knew we would never match "Pure And Simple" because that was such a phenomenon.'

Danny: 'I think there was definitely a feeling among some people that we would be one-hit wonders. Some people saw Pure And Simple go to number one at the end of the series and thought, "Fantastic end to a great story – you'll never hear from them again." We would never have let that happen. Yeah, we loved doing the programme, it was a great platform for us, but we all wanted to be in a band in the long term and we were never going to disappear after one single.'

Myleene: 'After the series if we'd just rested on our laurels and thought, "Yeah, number one single, record-breaking sales," we wouldn't have done ourselves any favours. It was important to us to last and to have success without the help of *Popstars*. We do feel that getting a second number one is a turning point because we achieved it on our own merit. We can hold our heads high.'

Danny: 'The day we heard we'd got to number one we'd got in really late after doing G.A.Y. so I'd spent the morning in bed. I got up around 2 p.m. and there was a text message from Chris, our manager, saying it looked like we'd got to number one, so that put a huge smile on my face. Then Noel got up, we played some music, and we all spoke to each other and decided we'd meet up at Suzy's that night.

'I went round to my nan's for a bit, then Suzy came and picked us up and it was when we were in the car listening to the radio that we heard the chart, which was cool but kind of surreal. After that we went to Suzy's and just had a good night. We were all there and the guys from Stargate came round. It was good because we were able to sit down and enjoy the moment. With Pure And Simple we got to number one then jumped straight onto limo bikes and went off to do a live interview. There wasn't time for anything to sink in.

TIME CHECK

Pure and Simple is the fastest-selling debut single ever. The fastest-selling single is Elton John's Candle in the Wind.

From the stage, we could see people climbing up the walls and sitting on window ledges.

'Don't get me wrong – it's brilliant to be busy, but this time was so good because we were all together just having a good time and reminiscing.'

Myleene: 'When I got home from G.A.Y. at 5 a.m., it was already light. I went to bed, then my phone beeped at me with a text message saying we'd made it to number one. I got up and went round to my mum's and in the afternoon I rang Dr Fox at Capital Radio and pre-recorded a message for him to play with the chart rundown later on. Then I went to a party at a friend's place and nipped out to the car at 7 p.m. to catch it on the radio. I drove over to Suzy's and we just sat there as five mates and celebrated. It was brilliant. We must have been noisy because we got told off by the neighbours!'

Noel: 'We always say it, but we couldn't do it without the support of the fans. They are amazing. You go to signings and there are thousands of people queuing round the block for hours just to see you. I find that overwhelming. I just don't get it. We did a signing in Oxford Street for the first single on the day it was released and there were something like 3,500 people in the queue – and some of them had been there eight hours. You can't take it in because it's so unreal. The fans who've touched me the most though are my little cousins, Joel and Luke. It's just the way their eyes light up when they see you. They're really cool. Joel goes round telling everyone he's my cousin and Luke's in awe of it all.'

Myleene: 'You can barely fathom the reaction when people turn up at signings. We did one in Coventry and there were so many people there. What was really touching was that almost every person brought us flowers. We ended up with crates filled with bunches of carnations. It's unbelievable that people will take the trouble to buy you a present or write you a letter. My mum is my number one fan. She keeps every cutting – it's like a Hear'say shrine in our house. She is just so proud.'

Kym: 'The idea of having fans, people who make an effort to see you, feels strange. And ours range from very young children to the over-sixties. It's a really good feeling when people come up and just say, "Well done, how are your kids?" Then you get some who just scream at you. They shake and have tears running down their face.

The view from the stage.

This is what it's all about, live performances – the best!

Just to touch you means so much to them, and that's bizarre. We have some fantastic fans. There are two girls called Becky and Kelly who always wear "Noel Pick Me" T-shirts when they come to anything. They're cool girls. They bought me a lovely diamanté necklace and earrings for my birthday, which I can wear on stage. I'm lucky, I get lots of presents, and people send my children things.

'The one thing that does disturb me is that I've had letters from girls who self-harm because they're going through a lot of trauma. One girl has lost someone close to her and she has started hurting herself because she feels partly to blame. It's so sad – she needs someone to talk to and she looks to me, which is scary, because I can't be there for her. There is nothing I can do for that girl. When she comes to signings all I can do is hug her. It's really tragic.'

Noel: 'I think we have a broad fan base because of *Popstars*. It's the first time parents have really seen the process of making a band and they've been able to get involved. They've seen the work we did and got to know the kind of people we are. Maybe in the past their kids have liked bands and they haven't really related to them or to the music, but they seem to feel differently about us.'

7.0

Danny: 'You appreciate the level of support when you go and perform. We played at a festival in the Northeast in the summer and that was just amazing. It was a Bank Holiday Monday and we flew up to Newcastle that morning not really knowing what to expect. The funny thing is, you tend to think the support is just in London because that's where we spend most of our time; then we go to other cities and just get blown away.

'When we got off the plane there were people waiting for us, so straight away we got a warm welcome. Then we got into cars and headed off to North Shields. On the way to the venue we picked up a police escort and there was a police helicopter overhead. Suddenly there were sirens and flashing lights and it was like, What's going on? We were all thinking it was a bit over the top but when we got close to the site we realized we needed it. The place was absolutely packed! We would never have got there without an escort. That was down to Tony Myers from Polydor in Newcastle. The funny thing is, he got separated from the convoy and got completely stuck in the traffic, which proved the point. The police had to go back and rescue him.'

Myleene: 'It was hilarious. There was this six-car cavalcade with a helicopter shadowing us and a police car stopping traffic for us. We were all just laughing our heads off. We thought we were being treated like royalty but, in fact, it was the only way to get us to the venue. When we actually arrived it was overwhelming – they didn't just come to see us, they came to support us. People had made banners for us and there were all these flags waving. It made me feel really humble.'

Noel: 'I arrived in Newcastle nursing a broken hand. I'd been messing round with a mate a couple of days before and he rugby-tackled me and broke my fingers. They were strapped up and I was supposed to be wearing a sling but I took it off because I didn't really want people to spot it. The press had heard anyway, so the others strapped up their fingers, too, just to confuse them. It didn't work! I just didn't think it was a story but the press did. One reporter tried to claim that I'd been given

There were so many people at the Newcastle gig that we had to take a lifeboat out, so we could catch our plane.

special treatment at the hospital that treated me, which wasn't true. It seemed a lot of fuss over a very small thing.'

Suzanne: 'The atmosphere in the Northeast was amazing. I love performing and outdoor gigs are the best. We were waiting backstage to go on and there were people who hadn't been able to get in waving at us through the fence. The site was right on the edge of the River Tyne and there were people on boats shouting and waving. We had an idea it was going to be a bit special.

'When we went on stage we got such an amazing welcome. There were Hear'say banners and everyone was singing along. You could see people actually hanging out of windows in the houses opposite and climbing onto window ledges to get a better view. It was fantastic. We did two tracks – "Pure And Simple" and "The Way To Your Love" and the plan was that we'd then do some press interviews and leave. But the crowd went so mad we ended up going back on and doing "The Way To Your Love" as an encore.'

Danny: 'What is it about the people in Newcastle? The support was unbelievable. We'd played our first outdoor gig in Swansea a few weeks earlier in front of about 80,000 people and the crowd was a fraction of the size in North Shields, but they

Noel and Suzanne share a Titanic moment.

TIME CHECK

Myleene once sang backing vocals for Cliff Richard. Cliff had his first hit in 1958 with Move It.

made more noise, I'm sure. I know that sounds ridiculous but that's how it felt. It was really mad and just brilliant.'

Kym: 'The funniest thing about the Northeast was that after we'd performed, the only way to get us out of the venue was by lifeboat! So the Tynemouth lifeboat crew picked us up and whisked us away down the river. I normally hate boats but it was really good fun.'

Danny: 'We had to get back to the airport for a flight back to London that afternoon so we had to move it. The lifeboat was our only chance really. We had all these boats and jet skis chasing us. The police launch was out too! We got dropped further along the river where our cars had been taken, then we raced back to the airport – only to find that our flight had been delayed! That whole event gave me a taste of what it's going to be like, touring. That's going to be fantastic and we're going to put on a good show. Everyone who comes to see us will want to be there and there will be no negativity in the arenas. It's just going to be a massive party. I think there will be some nerves and it will be emotional. We'll all cry. Our families will cry. I just think for a lot of people associated with Hear'say it's going to be a proud moment.'

(left and this page) On stage at G.A.Y. We found out The Way To Your Love had got to number one when we got home.

7.0

Kym: 'The buzz at an event like that is like nothing else. You see thousands of people screaming for you and you can barely believe it. A year before we weren't even a band! That kind of festival makes me realize how great it will be to tour. Performing live and meeting the fans is what we're all about. That's the most important thing. All we want to do is give the best we can every time we go on stage.'

Myleene: 'When you see people who've made an effort to come and see you, it means something. You feel like you've become part of their lives. It's extraordinary and it's moving. I remember being in Woolworths at a signing and hearing the chanting outside – "We want Hear'say!" – getting louder and louder. It brought tears to my eyes. And going on stage to a fantastic reception is an amazing feeling. When I think about the tour, playing to thousands of people in different places, I just know it's going to be special. For me, the idea of playing Wembley is something I never dared even dream about. My family will be there and I will just be so proud.'

Twenty minutes feels like one second when you're performing. We've enjoyed every single one of our Festival performances.

Kym: 'We have had some amazing experiences and met some brilliant people. I was so star struck when I met Geoffrey from *Rainbow*! It took me right back to my childhood and brought back so many memories. We met Mohamed Al Fayed who was really cool and took us out to lunch. And we met Prince Charles too. I expected Prince Charles to be stuffy but he was pretty down-to-earth. He seemed like a really nice guy, the kind of person you could have a laugh with. He said, "I like your T-shirt – armed and dangerous." He could have had it, but I couldn't really see him wearing

it...! We met Anastacia and she was so friendly. You usually find that the bigger the star the nicer the person. She was beautiful. There are some people I really liked before all this happened – some I fancied – and I very quickly changed my mind when I met them. My biggest heroes are my parents. They're my number one fans – and my kids, of course.'

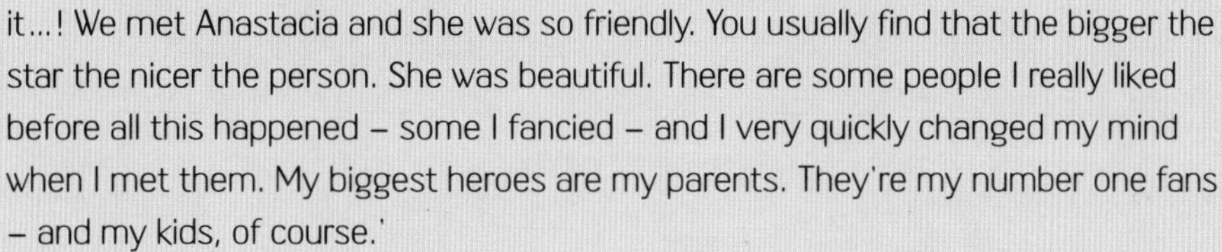

Noel: 'I admire more people now because I realize how hard it is to do this. Anastacia's now on my list and Robbie Williams and Steps. They work so hard and they've done really well for themselves – they're a nice bunch too. I met Tom Jones recently and he's such a big hero of mine that I just went to pieces! Apparently, I went white. I was walking down this corridor and a big entourage came in and he walked past. One of his people was someone I'd met before and he said, "Tom, it's Noel from Hear'say..." He turned round and shook my hand and said "How you doing?" I was like, "Oh my God." I met Prince Charles too and he said, "I saw a banner with 'Noel is fit' on it and it amused me!" Sometimes when you stop and look at what we're doing it's quite amazing. I still don't feel like we're part of that world now, not at all. It feels like we're just blagging!'

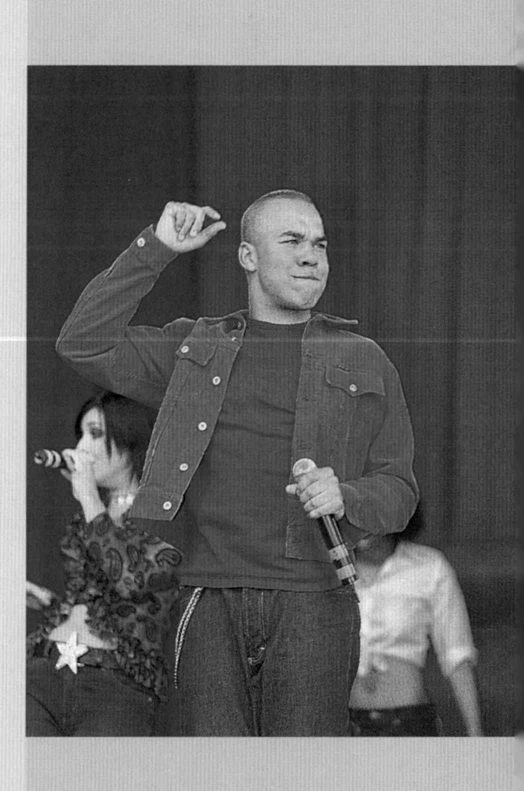

LOOKING TO THE FUTURE

8

Danny: 'I just hope we can keep it together with all the pressure ... I just want us to be happy. Happiness is the ultimate thing.'

Suzanne: 'A year from now I'd love to have a villa in Switzerland. When we went there I couldn't get over how beautiful it is. I would love to be able to take my family away on holiday and treat them. I'd love to have horses as well. A bit further ahead I'd also love to be an actress again. This is my job now and I've got to concentrate on it, but my first ever ambition was to go to Hollywood and be an actress and I'd love to do that. That would be my ultimate dream. I wanted to be a pop star and an actress, and if I ever achieve both I could never complain.'

TIME CHECK

David Cassidy was a guest on Hear'say's new TV show. He was a huge 70s heartthrob and star of the American sitcom The Partridge Family.

(this page and right) The guys on the set of their television programme Hear'say: It's Saturday.

Myleene: 'A year from now I'd like to have taken my mum and dad and my brother and sister for a holiday, if it's practical for us all to get away together. I'd love to buy my mum and dad a house. In terms of the band, I'd love for Hear'say to be breaking new territories. I would hope we'd be as strong then as we are now and for the Hear'say flag to still be flying. I'd also like to be doing more songwriting.'

Noel: 'A year from now I'd still like to be doing this, for us still to be together and strong. I'd love for us to do what the Spice Girls did and break everywhere. That was such a phenomenal achievement. I'd like to do a lot more writing and to work with producers who encourage that because we're new to it and need to be nurtured.'

Kym: 'In a year's time, I would love to be living with my children and my parents, probably in London. It's a huge goal for me to get my parents a house and I will do it, but it takes time. I'd like to be looking to break America, to win some Brit Awards and have some Smash Hits Awards under our belt, to be working on the second album, and making progress in Europe.'

Danny: 'A year from now I'd definitely like Hear'say to still be making great music, for us to be writing a lot more, and for the next album to be successful. I'd also like to see us as a group, still working well together. I just hope we can keep it together with all the pressure. If a year down the line we're still a solid five, I'll be happy. I'd like to have a bit of money – not tons, just a bit – so I could treat my family, and buy myself a flat outright. I just want us all to be happy. Happiness is the ultimate thing.'